The Geometry
of Incidence

The
GEOMETRY
of
INCIDENCE

Harold L. Dorwart

SEABURY PROFESSOR OF MATHEMATICS
TRINITY COLLEGE, HARTFORD, CONNECTICUT

Prentice–Hall, Inc.
ENGLEWOOD CLIFFS, NEW JERSEY

PRENTICE-HALL INTERNATIONAL, INC.   *London*
PRENTICE-HALL OF AUSTRALIA, PTY., LTD.   *Sydney*
PRENTICE-HALL OF CANADA, LTD.   *Toronto*
PRENTICE-HALL OF INDIA (PRIVATE), LTD.   *New Delhi*
PRENTICE-HALL OF JAPAN, INC.   *Tokyo*

To Carolyn

Contents

I

Fundamental Notions 1

II

The Real Projective Plane 45

III

Some Theorems of Plane Projective Geometry 81

IV

The General Projective Plane and Finite Projective Planes 121

Preface

FOR ROUGHLY two thousand years after Euclid—in 330–320 B.C.—collected and organized the material that makes up his famous *Elements*, this work *was* geometry. This statement does not mean that no original contributions were made during this long period or that no individuals existed who were worthy of the title of geometer, but, by and large, Euclid dominated the field of geometry.

In the seventeenth and eighteenth centuries the names of Descartes, Fermat, Desargues, Pascal, Monge, Euler, and others were associated with new developments that formed the beginnings of subjects that sooner or later were to be called Analytic Geometry, Differential Geometry, Projective Geometry, Descriptive Geometry, Topology, and other such names.

Then in the nineteenth century came the great explosion in geometry, the period that has been described by Coolidge (15)† as

---

† References are to the Bibliography on p. 148.

ix

the "Heroic Age of Geometry." One hesitates to mention any names in this connection since the list would immediately grow to unmanageable length and would be meaningless anyway without a description of the achievements of these individuals. Such lists and descriptions are readily available in other works.[†]

However, one cannot make even a brief reference to the mathematical history of the nineteenth century without mentioning the revolutionary work of Bolyai, Lobachewsky, Riemann, and their successors in founding the non-Euclidean geometries. This in turn focused attention on the postulational approach in mathematics—first in geometry and later in algebra and other fields—and thus paved the way for the twentieth-century explosion in mathematics which for descriptive purposes may well be classed as of thermonuclear magnitude.[‡]

With the current emphasis on generalization and on abstract mathematics, together with the demand for mathematicians trained in fields that formerly would have been called applied mathematics or even have been considered to be parts of other disciplines, higher geometry has lost ground as a subject for study. This is deplored by groups of mathematicians who are concerned with curricular reform in the schools and colleges and by many individual mathematicians. Herbert Busemann has recently made a strong plea for the inclusion of projective geometry in the undergraduate mathematics curriculum:

> *The subject is beautiful, it required major efforts of some of the best mathematicians during and after the last century to understand its structure thoroughly, it still gives a deep insight into geometry. The projective duality principle, besides being constantly used by geometers, is an exciting experience for any interested student. The duality in vector*

[†] For example, see Meserve *48* Chap. 7, or Bell *9*.

[‡] See Stone *66*.

spaces is a very meager substitute. But most of all, do we have the right to completely disrupt historical continuity whenever a subject moves out of the focus of contemporary interests? Do we really expect or agree that our present mathematical efforts will be altogether junked (at least from courses) as soon as the interests change? This disregard for historical continuity obviously leads to dangerous absurdities if taken seriously and must be fought. As far as geometry is concerned the speaker believes that projective geometry is a subject on which to make a stand. A mathematics major should not obtain his degree without knowing projective geometry.[†]

A. Seidenberg has stated:

Aside from the intrinsic interest of projective geometry, there is the fact that the main events of algebraic geometry, one of the principal branches of mathematics, take place in projective spaces. Therefore projective spaces are "something everyone has to know."[‡]

A very readable amplification of this point of view is found in Jenner (*39*).

How can interest in geometry—specifically in projective geometry—be revived? Perhaps a new type of book is needed, one that selects certain fundamental concepts and theorems having relevance in present-day mathematics and that discusses these concepts and theorems in considerable detail and with some historical perspective. The content should be so chosen that the reader will actually be able to *do* some easy mathematics before too long, but no attempt should be made to tell him everything. He should not be misled by over-simplification, and perhaps the best way to avoid this is to give a fairly extensive bibliography and a list of notes concerned with further developments. The hope would be to arouse his curiosity to such an extent that he would

---

[†] *14*, p. 283.
[‡] *61*, Preface, p. v.

then consult at least some of the references. These references should be to specific portions of easily read and readily available literature which in turn would contain other references to original sources, to alternative procedures, and to some current fields of research. Thus, the book would not be a textbook in the ordinary sense, but it might serve as an introduction or as a guide for individual study. The need for such books will doubtless become apparent as the reforms in secondary school curricula proceed, as the ratio of the increasing number of college students taking mathematics courses to the number of qualified instructors available increases, and as more and more adults have time for, and develop interests in, fields of intellectual endeavor.

The present book is an attempt to write something of this nature. If it has any merit, credit should probably be given to what will be called (1) the Penguin Principle, (2) the Klein Criteria, and (3) Descartes' Directions.

The Penguin Principle is distilled in an obvious manner from the story of the girl who asked a librarian for a book on penguins. She was given a large and scholarly work, which she returned the next day with the comment, "This book is no good." The baffled librarian explained that the book had been written by an authority on penguins and wanted to know why the girl thought it was no good. The immediate reply was, "It tells me more about penguins than I care to know."

The German mathematician, Felix Klein (1849–1925), was interested in the training of teachers of mathematics and has written for them a multiple-volume work called *Elementary Mathematics from an Advanced Standpoint*. The first volume is concerned with arithmetic, algebra, and analysis, and the second volume, with geometry (*41*). In a final section of the second volume, entitled "Foundations of Geometry," Klein expresses himself concerning the source and origin of the "leading concepts and statements" of geometry in a manner that some present-day mathematicians will probably consider hopelessly old-fashioned, but for which others will have considerable sympathy as they look back somewhat nostalgically on the days when mathematics appeared to be considerably less complicated.

After giving his view that "*fundamental concepts and axioms are not immediately facts of perception, but are appropriately selected idealizations of these facts,*" Klein then states another point of view:

> *In contrast with this, one finds frequently now, on the part of persons who are interested only in the logical side of things and not in the side of perception or of the general theory of knowledge, the opinion that* the axioms are only arbitrary statements which we set up at pleasure and the fundamental concepts, likewise, are only arbitrary symbols for things with which we operate. ... [*This leads*] *in the direction of that philosophy which has long been called* nominalism. *Here interest in things themselves and their properties is entirely lost. What is discussed is the way things are named, and the logical scheme according to which one operates with the names. ... For one, I cannot share this point of view. I regard it, rather, as the death of all science.* The axioms of geometry are—according to my way of thinking—not arbitrary, but sensible statements, which are, in general, induced by space perception and are determined as to their precise content by expediency.[†]

A somewhat similar view of mathematics is expressed by Courant and Robbins:

> *A serious threat to the very life of science is implied in the assertion that mathematics is nothing but a system of conclusions drawn from definitions and postulates that must be consistent but otherwise may be created by the free will of the mathematician. If this description were accurate, mathematics could not attract any intelligent person. It would*

---

† Klein *41*, p. *187*.

be a game with definitions, rules, and syllogisms, without motive or
goal. The notion that the intellect can create meaningful postulational
systems at its whim is a deceptive half-truth. Only under the discipline
of responsibility to the organic whole, only guided by intrinsic necessity,
can the free mind achieve results of scientific value.[†]

A small number of fundamental concepts and axioms (or
"postulates" in modern terminology) have been selected for
discussion in this book, and a considerable effort will be made
to show where they come from and the "expediency" that has
caused them to take their present form. Furthermore, for the sake
of simplicity, the discussion will be largely limited to the plane,
that is, to a space of two dimensions.

In 1637 the French mathematician and philosopher René
Descartes (1596–1650) published his celebrated work *La géomé-*
trie,[‡] which was favorably received, particularly by the younger
generation of mathematicians of that period, and which today
is mentioned in the opening paragraph of every textbook on
analytic geometry. Two years later an architect of Lyons named
Girard Desargues (1593–1662) published a brief treatise on conic
sections which contained much original material of high quality.
Unfortunately, Desargues' style of writing, and the large number
of new terms (some seventy odd) that he introduced, made his
book almost unreadable, even to prominent mathematicians of
that period who were his friends.

One of these was Descartes, who, in a letter to Desargues,
offered some advice. After stating that, if an author is writing for
the professionals in mathematics, he should use only the symbols
and terms that have gained general acceptance, he then indicates

---

[†] *16*, p. xvii.

[‡] One of three appendices to his *Discours de la méthode pour bien conduire sa*
raison et chercher la vérité dans les sciences.

that terms such as Desargues used, which were "conceived with spirit and grace," might find favor in a popular account. He goes on to say:

> *But, if you have that intention, you should make of it a great volume; explain it all so fully and so distinctly that those gentlemen who cannot study without yawning; who cannot distress their imaginations enough to grasp a proposition in geometry, nor turn the leaves of a book to look at the letters in a figure, shall find nothing in your discourse more difficult to understand than the description of an enchanted palace in a fairy story.*[†]

These directions will not be followed literally, but an attempt will be made to recapture some of the enchantment felt a generation or two ago by many students of what might now be called classical geometry. This does not mean that an even greater enchantment cannot be experienced by students of modern geometry *if they persevere sufficiently*. First, however, they must obtain a broad background in modern abstract algebra—a vast and rapidly growing field—and thereby acquire a taste for generalization and abstraction. To give some idea of what this means, we describe briefly a recently published book whose title is *Continuous Geometry*.

Continuous geometry was invented in 1935 by the late John von Neumann, and the book reproduces his lecture notes together with a Foreword and editorial remarks by Israel Halperin. The book contains 295 pages, but pictures or figures appear on only six of these pages, in appendices to certain chapters where "The reader is asked to remember that these pictures are of value only heuristically...." The Foreword contains the statement, "It is easy to see that in a continuous geometry there can be

---

[†] See Lehmer *44*, p. 106.

no minimal element—that is, no atomic element or *point*."[†]
Although some geometric terms are used (with generalized
meanings), even a mathematician thumbing through the book
without looking at the title would probably think he was examining a treatise on modern abstract algebra. Certainly such a book is
vastly different from the books on geometry that were published
during the early part of the present century.[‡]

As indicated earlier, this book is not a textbook in the usual
sense, and—since it contains some actual mathematics—it is not a
popular account. The following questions now arise. First, what
are the prerequisites for reading the book with a fair degree of
understanding? And second, for whom is the book written?

Without equivocation it must be stated that the reader will
need some degree of familiarity with analytic geometry. He will
not, however, need a detailed knowledge of the subject. The
residue that remains from a college course taken some years ago or
the introduction to analytic methods that is usually given at the
present time in advanced high school courses will serve ade-
quately. Although extensive use will be made of certain algebraic
concepts, these are introduced in such a way that very little previous knowledge is assumed. If the reader can follow the solution
of two simultaneous linear (i.e. first degree) equations in two
unknowns and then can apply the definition of a second order
determinant

$$\begin{vmatrix} A & B \\ C & D \end{vmatrix} = AD - BC,$$

he will find that he can understand the proofs of the theorems
given in this book. In Section 1.4 an illustrative example makes use

---

[†] Von Neumann *68*, p. v.
[‡] E.g. Graustein *28*, Veblen and Young *67*, Winger *70*, Woods *72*.

of the simultaneous solution of two quadratic equations and the discriminant condition for the equality of the two roots of a quadratic equation, but, as is stated in a footnote there, it should be possible for the reader to get the gist of the example without following all of the algebraic details. Of course, the reader with a greater knowledge of algebra will be able to discern additional connections with topics merely hinted at, but we repeat that this greater knowledge is not necessary for the immediate objectives.

Thus, the book should be intelligible to the high-school student who is taking a senior mathematics course, to persons enrolled in teacher training courses in mathematics, and to scientists or college graduates in fields related to mathematics who have some knowledge of and interest in mathematics. In addition, it is hoped that the book will prove to be helpful to college students, either as an introduction to a course in projective geometry or as collateral reading for mathematics majors who do not have the time or opportunity to take such a course.

The book is probably too difficult for the so-called "layman in mathematics," although the writer is not certain of this. For example, many parents as a matter of self-defense are currently studying "modern mathematics." Some of them are making considerable progress and—to their surprise—are actually enjoying what they are doing. Unfortunately, there is no royal road to success in mathematics, but many people with a liking for the subject have learned later in life that not all mathematics is as difficult as they may have suspected from school or college courses and, furthermore, that the time and effort spent in mastering new concepts can result in considerable intellectual pleasure.

HAROLD L. DORWART

Hartford, Connecticut

*The Geometry
of Incidence*

I

Fundamental Notions

1.1 Introduction

Three basic or primitive concepts that will be used repeatedly in this book are *point*, *line*, and *incidence*. We shall begin by assuming that the reader presently feels no need for a discussion of the first two (After all, everyone *knows* that a point is just "the idealized limit of a smaller and smaller material dot," etc.) and shall concentrate on the third.

The English noun *incidence* comes from the Latin verb *incidere*, from *in* meaning in or on, plus *cadere*, to fall. When we say that a point is incident with a line, we shall mean merely that the point falls on or *lies on* the line. Likewise, a line will be said to be incident with a point when the line falls on or *passes through* the point. Here also, we assume that *lies on* and *passes through* convey meaning to the reader without further discussion.

To get some idea of why such a concept as incidence is introduced, we now consider two simple geometric figures in the
plane (Figures 1 and 2). If one were asked to describe these figures,
he might make such statements as:

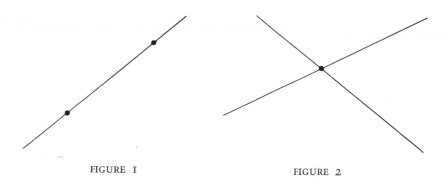

FIGURE I   FIGURE 2

One and only one line passes
through any two distinct points.

Or:

Exactly one line is incident
with every two distinct points.

Two distinct lines always intersect in one and only one point
(unless the lines are parallel).

Or:

Exactly one point is incident
with every two distinct lines (unless the lines are parallel).

Although most readers would not notice it, there is a certain
type of resemblance between the two figures. Figure 1 consists
of two geometric elements of one kind (points) and one element
of a second kind (a line), while Figure 2 is in reverse so to speak.
It consists of two lines and one point. The first pair of descriptions,
using the phrases "passes through" and "intersect in," are, of
course, common descriptions. They tend, however, to emphasize
a difference rather than a resemblance in the two situations.

On the other hand, the phraseology of the second pair of descriptions, using the expression "is incident with," not only helps to bring out the resemblance but also will turn out to be very helpful later. Very soon we shall discover that there is a type of geometry in which, for every statement and proof of a theorem, the statement and proof of another (sometimes startlingly strange) theorem will be right at our finger tips. If we use the incidence (or an equivalent) terminology, the new theorem and its proof can be obtained from the old by merely interchanging the words (or symbols for) "point" and "line."†

An indulgent reader has probably gone along with the discussion thus far, but about now he looks back and sees the additional phrase, in parentheses in the right-hand descriptions, "unless the lines are parallel." He then realizes that when we are talking about any two lines in the plane, Figure 2 should probably be labeled Figure 2(a), and that for the sake of completeness the additional figure, Figure 2(b), should be included. How can

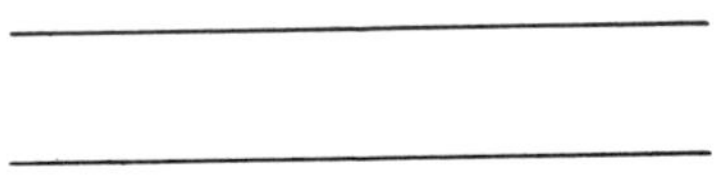

FIGURE 2(b)

there be any real resemblance between the left and right sides with this awkward qualification on the right side?

Stepping up to three distinct points and lines in the plane, we find that the situation is still worse (Figures 3 and 4).

---

† This is an instance of something called "plane duality" which will be discussed in the third section of Chap. II.

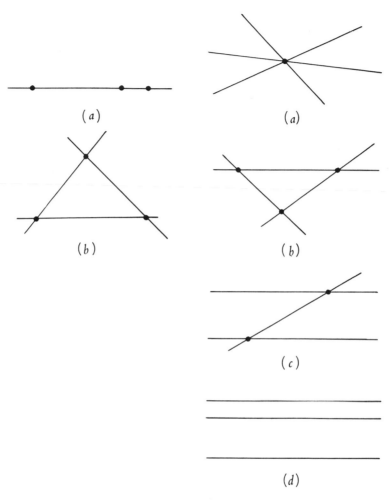

FIGURE 3

Three distinct points are always either (a) incident with one line (i.e. are collinear), or (b) incident by pairs with three lines (i.e. form a triangle).

FIGURE 4

Three distinct lines are always either (a) incident with one point (i.e. are concurrent), or (b) incident by pairs with three points (i.e. form a triangle), unless (c) exactly two of the lines are parallel, or (d) all three lines are parallel.

4

If one can clearly understand the steps taken by geometers a century or so ago in removing from plane geometry the awkward special cases caused by parallel lines (Remember that there are no parallel points, i.e. no points without a line in common), thus obtaining a more general kind of geometry, he has gone a long way toward an appreciation of the spirit of modern abstract postulational mathematics. For most people such an understanding requires a leisurely approach with detailed explanations. This will be the main function of Chapter I after some rather general discussion in the next section.

I.2   *Klein's Classification of Geometries*

The title of this book is frankly designed to be eye-catching, but it is also intended to be descriptive. Although the preface and first section have given some clues as to the content of the book, the reader may welcome additional orientation before he goes further.

Euclidean plane geometry is one of the oldest portions of mathematics, and it is also a subject concerning which almost everyone feels that he has some knowledge. Statements in the preface of this book indicate that a great amount of geometry has been constructed since the time of Euclid that is not a part of his geometry. Thus there appears to be a need for some kind of a classification scheme. Before discussing such a scheme, however, it may be of interest to consider how present-day writers relate geometry to mathematics as a whole.

One writer has stated:

> *Nowadays most mathematicians would define geometry as any part of mathematics in which utterances are made which sound like geometry. If this answer is open to objection on logical grounds, which manifestly*

is the case, the same is also true of the question [Is algebraic geometry, especially when done over arbitrary fields, really geometry?] Nevertheless, the intent of this " definition" is certainly clear enough and comes about as close to the right spirit as one could hope for.[†]

A second writer makes the following statement:

... today perhaps geometry more properly describes a point of view— a way of looking at a subject—than it does any one part of mathematics.[‡]

If this is a trifle unsettling, let us take as much comfort as we can from the qualifying "perhaps" and continue for the present at least with the traditional idea that geometry is "the study of the properties of figures in the plane or space."

How can we subdivide geometry, or how characterize different parts of the subject? In the past, the terms "synthetic" and "analytic"—the first referring to the axiomatic procedure of Euclid, and the second to the introduction of numerical co-ordinates—were sometimes used as if they described different parts of geometry rather than different *methods* for studying the same part, the current usage of these terms. Such a title as "differential geometry" is used to describe the study of space curves and surfaces, with the calculus (including vector and tensor calculus) as the principal *tool*. "Algebraic geometry," however, also studies curves and surfaces but primarily with the use of algebra (both classical algebra and modern abstract algebra). Thus we see that methods of procedure or principal tools used, although helpful in describing texts or courses, do not characterize *content* in geometry.

Most readers know that something called *non-Euclidean*

[†] Jenner *39*, p. 26.
[‡] Blumenthal *12*, Preface, p. v.

geometry[1] † was invented or discovered during the nineteenth
century. Hence the two expressions Euclidean geometry and non-
Euclidean geometry would certainly appear to give a classification of *all* geometry into two distinct and non-overlapping
categories. Unhappily, when mathematicians use the expression
non-Euclidean geometry, they use it in a much more restrictive
sense than might be imagined and refer only to a geometry that
uses a postulate other than the one (or its equivalent) used by
Euclid when dealing with the thorny matter of parallel lines.
Since a large portion of what is currently called geometry is able
to ignore completely not only the concept of parallel lines but
also the concept of distance, which plays an important part in
much of Euclid's geometry, there remains for the mathematician
a large part of geometry that cannot conveniently be classified
as either Euclidean or non-Euclidean.

In 1872 the German mathematician Felix Klein wrote an
address for presentation on entering the Philosophical Faculty and
the Senate at the University of Erlangen. This address was published at Erlangen but had a limited circulation for some years.
Shortly after an Italian translation had appeared, an English translation with the title "A Comparative Review of Recent Re-
searches in Geometry" was published in July, 1893 in Volume
II of the *Bulletin of the New York Mathematical Society*. This paper
contains not only a neat way of classifying as to *content* all of the
geometry that was known toward the end of the nineteenth
century but also the definition of *a* geometry. Although in his
introduction Klein modestly states,

In undertaking in the following pages to establish such a principle, we

---

† References given in this fashion with superior numerals are to the Notes
beginning on page 141.

shall hardly develop an essentially new idea, but rather formulate clearly what has already been more or less definitely conceived by many others,[†]

this classification and definition have become known as Klein's "Erlanger Programm" for geometry.

Instead of reproducing Klein's statement of his "principle," it will probably be wiser to quote a modern restatement.

A geometry is the study of the properties of a set S which remain invariant when the elements of set S are subjected to the transformations of some transformation group.[‡]

The words "set," "invariant," "transformations," and "transformation group" are all technical terms in mathematics and as such have precise definitions. Many readable discussions of these definitions, together with simple illustrative examples, are given in other works.[2] Fortunately, if we regard "set" as a synonym for collection, the technical meanings are not too far removed from some everyday usages of these words, and we shall attempt, in an informal manner, to shed some light on Klein's definition and classification scheme.

First, however, we should say that in the twentieth century new creations in mathematics called *abstract spaces*[3] have led to some very general systems that probably should be called geometries but which do not come under Klein's classification. This should in no way detract from the importance of Klein's contribution, which broadened earlier concepts, codified existing geometries, and paved the way for other discoveries.[4]

In passing, we might also comment on the fact that Klein's

[†] Klein later expanded his presentation and included it in a book that is now available in paperback form (Klein *41*).

[‡] Eves and Newsom *23*, p. 135.

definition is for *a* geometry rather than for geometry in general. Because he has previously heard of non-Euclidean geometry, the reader is probably not so surprised to learn of the existence of still other geometries as he was (or will be) when he first learned (or learns) that there are many different algebras.

In Figure 5 we give the Klein classification chart for certain geometries that will be discussed informally in the remaining paragraphs of this section.

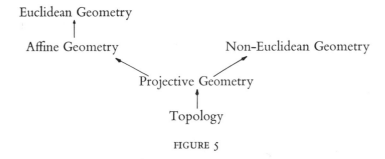

FIGURE 5

In this hierarchical arrangement, three names appear that are probably new to many readers: topology, projective geometry, and affine geometry. If he has heard of topology, the reader is doubtless aware that it is a relatively new branch of mathematics, and he probably wonders why the arrows start at topology and (on the left) end with the ancient subject of Euclidean geometry. For a historical discussion, the direction of the arrows would be reversed. Here, our purpose is to indicate that with Klein's classification in mind, topology is the most general or the deepest geometry. The theorems of topology are valid in each of the other geometries, but in general the theorems of projective geometry are not a part of topology, the theorems of affine geometry are not a part of projective geometry, etc. In other words, what we ordinarily call Euclidean geometry, when examined from Klein's point of view, will emerge as a rather complicated and highly specialized subject.

The above statement is meant to be mildly reassuring to the reader who considers himself to be a reasonably astute individual but who may have had some difficulty with high-school geometry. At the same time, it is hoped that those readers who "breezed through" such a course in secondary school will now begin to suspect that there may be more to geometry than they have previously realized. Incidently, a fascinating diversion at this point would be to consider the "flaws" in Euclid's treatment of geometry and the reforms that are currently taking place in the teaching of high-school geometry.[†] Also, the reader will doubtless be surprised to learn that, from Klein's point of view, Euclidean geometry is not a pure-strain geometry but is actually a combination of several geometries.[‡]

We now return to the starting point on our chart and ask the question "What is topology?" A well-known topologist, R. H. Bing, in a readable monograph that is highly recommended to the reader, begins by saying "In many respects, topology may be considered an offshoot of geometry," and then later states, "Topology may be defined as a study of properties that remain invariant under homeomorphisms."[§] This statement, containing the phrases "study of properties" and "remain invariant," certainly reminds us of Klein's definition of a geometry and appears to justify calling topology a geometry.[††]

But what are *homeomorphisms*? The root meaning of the word, "of like form," doesn't help us very much here. Actually

---

[†] See Fishback *25*, pp. 1–8.
[‡] See Coxeter *19*, p. 175 ff.
[§] Bing *10*
[††] See Blumenthal *11*, p. 32.

Professor Bing does not give his definition of topology until page 27 of the 58-page monograph, the earlier pages being devoted to a discussion of other concepts leading up to the technical definition of homeomorphism.[5] Even then, Bing qualifies his achievement by saying, "Perhaps it is best not to define topology to people who do not already know what it is"!

Going to an ordinary dictionary for the definition of a mathematical term is usually not particularly enlightening,[†] and sometimes it may even be misleading. However, let's risk it in the case of topology. Here we find: "*Math.* The doctrine of those properties of a figure unaffected by any deformation without tearing or joining."[‡] What kind of deformations would these be? At once we think of pulling or stretching and are led to the characterization of two-dimensional topology as "rubber-sheet geometry,"[§] i.e. as the geometry of lines and figures drawn on a rubber sheet.[6] For our purposes this will be highly satisfactory, but we warn the reader that Bing devotes several pages in the early portion of his monograph to showing, by means of examples, the insufficiency of the "pulling and stretching but without breaking or tearing" approach to topology.[††]

Realizing then that in our preliminary survey we are looking at topology through low-power binoculars, can we distinguish any property or properties of figures that are unchanged by pulling or stretching? Perhaps the best way to begin is by listing some properties that *are* changed. Certainly size and shape are not preserved. This means that straight lines do not necessarily remain

---

[†] See Niven *50*, pp. 5, 6.

[‡] *Webster's New International Dictionary of the English Language* (2nd Ed., Unabridged) (Springfield, Mass.: G. & C. Merriam Co., 1934).

[§] Kasner and Newman *40*, Chap. VIII.

[††] See also Arnold *4*, Chap. 1, or Delachet *21*, pp. 48–50.

straight lines under topological transformations as we have described them. However if two straight lines intersect in a point on our rubber sheet, the curves that will correspond to these straight lines after we have done as much pulling and stretching as we please (but with no tearing or joining) will still have one point in common. Thus we see that some (possibly highly refined) concept growing out of our idea of *incidence* of point and line (or point and curve) will be a topological invariant. Instead of following this further, of mentioning other topologically invariant properties, of discussing the many intriguing "topological oddities"[†] (" ... the true spirit of topology lies in proving theorems rather than in the oddities." Bing *10*, p. 2.), or of showing the importance of topology in modern mathematics[‡] ("Today the angel Topology and the demon Abstract Algebra struggle for the soul of each of the mathematical domains." Hermann Weyl[§]), we pass on to a brief discussion of projective and affine geometries.

Projective transformations[7] are special cases of topological transformations in which straight lines correspond to straight lines. To obtain a visualization of a projective transformation from one plane to another in space, we consider a coffee table with a glass top on which we have drawn two segments of straight lines AB and CD intersecting at point E (Figure 6).

If a source of light is placed at some point L above and behind the table, the reader—whether or not he has ever studied solid geometry—has little difficulty in imagining what the shadow of the intersecting segments will be on the floor. The point A will *project* into the point A' which is the intersection of the beam of

---

† See Meserve *48*, Chap. 9, or Arnold *4*.
‡ See Delachet *21*, p. 41.
§ Quoted in Félix *24*, p. 91.

light through A, i.e. the line through L and A, with the plane of
the floor. Likewise B projects into B' and the segment AB into
the segment $A'B'$ (the intersection of the plane of light through
L, A, and B with the floor plane). In similar fashion, CD projects
into $C'D'$ and E into E', i.e. points correspond to points, lines to
lines, and the incidence of point and line is preserved.

We have just described a *central* projection (center at L) from
one plane onto a parallel plane, i.e. from the top of the coffee
table onto the floor. By tipping the coffee table, we of course have
a central projection from one plane onto a non-parallel plane. A
little experimentation (changing the location of L) will not only
show that we can change the location of E' but will also quickly
convince us that two perpendicular lines on the coffee table will
not necessarily produce shadows that are at right angles, i.e. in
general, angles are not preserved under central projections
(Figure 7).

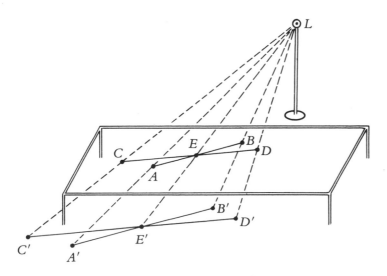

FIGURE 6

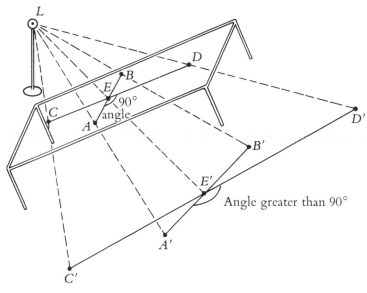

Angle greater than 90°

FIGURE 7

A particularly interesting location for *L* in the case of the tipped table is anywhere on a plane through *E* that is parallel to the floor. As *L* approaches this plane, say from above on the left-hand side of the table, the point *E'* moves out of sight on the right-hand side, and the shadows beginning at *A'* and *C'* approach parallelism (Figure 8).

Although a glass topped coffee table—or for that matter a simple pane of glass—provides a useful piece of laboratory equipment, restrictions have been imposed that we must now eliminate. The finite size of the glass forced us to talk about segments of lines (which suggest the concept of length or distance) rather than about lines of indefinite extent passing through two points such as *A* and *B*. The reader is now asked to replace (mentally) the glass by a plane of indefinite extent and to extend the segments on both ends. And finally, if we now discard the

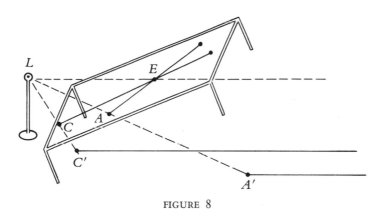

FIGURE 8

interpretation of L as a source of light and $A'B'$ as the shadow of AB on the floor, we can generalize our concept of central projection and our geometric construction so that AB may be thought of as the projection of $A'B'$ *from* the floor *onto* the table; i.e. we say that two figures in distinct planes are said to be derived from each other by *central projection* if corresponding points can be joined by *concurrent* lines, all passing through a fixed point L. Projective geometry may then be defined as the study of the properties of figures that are left invariant (i.e. unchanged) under central projections.[8]

We are now in a position to understand intuitively what is meant by the statement that all conic sections are projectively equivalent, i.e. that the different curves that are obtained by cutting the two nappes of a right, circular conical surface by a plane—the circles, ellipses, parabolas and hyperbolas—can be projected into one another by a central projection. The apparatus for demonstrating this is probably available in your living room. If you have a lamp with a shade that is roughly a portion of a right, circular cylinder, all you have to do is to turn off the other lights in the room and then observe the curves that mark off light from shade as you hold the lamp near a wall and tilt it in various ways. Light will issue from the top and bottom of the lamp as solid cones of light, and the wall will be the intersecting plane.

If you start with the axis of the lamp perpendicular to the wall, a circle of light will appear on the wall. When the axis is tipped slightly, this circle changes into an oval shape called the ellipse. With more tipping, the ellipse lengthens, and there is one particular position that will make the wall curve take the form of a parabola. Beyond this position, light from both ends of the cylindrical shade will shine on the wall creating the two branches of the hyperbola. This curve is particularly evident when the

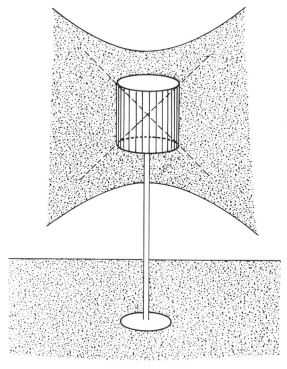

FIGURE 9

axis of the lamp is parallel to the wall (i.e. when the lamp is in the normal position as shown in Figure 9).

Although our primary study is to be of plane geometry, we have introduced the idea of central projection in space because this appears to be the more natural way of beginning. The mathematical definition of central projection given in an earlier paragraph can easily be modified for the plane. In doing this carefully, one has to avoid certain pitfalls such as the possibility of projecting a line into a point. We shall not concern ourselves with the fine details here. Actually, Figures 6, 7, and 8 are examples of plane central projections if one forgets the space figures that they represent.

Proofs of the theorems of projective geometry require us to set up carefully a system of definitions and postulates before we use the synthetic method, or to introduce some kind of numerical characterization of points and lines before we use the analytic method. It should be pointed out, however, that many important theorems were first surmised[†] in an experimental or intuitive manner, and that geometric intuition—although frowned upon by many mathematicians who are interested only in the rigorous methods of analysis—is still a valuable trait for a geometer.[9]

A slight modification of our apparatus for visualizing central projection in space will introduce us to *parallel projection* and thence to *affine geometry*, which may be defined as the study of the properties of figures unchanged under parallel projections. All we have to do is to replace the lamp bulb at L by the sun ! That is, two figures are said to be derived from each other by parallel projection if pairs of corresponding points can be joined by *parallel* lines. Strictly speaking, this would require the source of light in our visual aid to be infinitely distant. The sun, of course, is at a

---

† We shall give some examples in later chapters.

finite distance from the earth; but this distance is very great when judged by terrestial standards, and so, for practical purposes, when the sun casts a shadow of a small object on the ground, the rays of light may be considered to be parallel to each other.

In parallel projections, as in central projections, straight lines remain straight lines, and the incidence of point and line is preserved. However, size and shape are changed in parallel projection from one plane to another unless the two planes themselves are parallel. A little experimentation will disclose properties that are preserved under parallel projections but which are not invariant under central projections. Among these we note that parallel lines remain parallel, bisected segments remain bisected, and equal areas remain equal. Thus parallelism is a part of affine geometry— recall that it was unknown in projective geometry—but perpendicularity and distance are still undefined.

The classification of conics into ellipses, parabolas, and hyperbolas is an affine classification, i.e. these curves are not affinely equivalent as they were projectively equivalent. For example, an ellipse cannot be transformed into an hyperbola by an affine transformation (as it could be by a projective transformation). The circle, however, is not distinguishable from the ellipse in affine geometry. Circles as such are encountered for the first time when one introduces the concept of perpendicularity and the transformations called the rigid motions (the translations, rotations, etc. that form the principal group in Euclidean geometry).

As the reader probably suspects, part of Euclid's geometry is actually affine geometry. Also, he will discover later that when we attempt to visualize theorems of projective geometry, we shall usually do so in what is called the affine plane.

So far no mention has been made of the geometry mentioned in the title of this book—"incidence geometry." What is incidence geometry and where does it belong in Klein's classification?

At the beginning of the present century the great German mathematician, David Hilbert (1862–1943), formulated a set of postulates for plane (and also for solid) Euclidean geometry that satisfy current standards of rigor.[†] Hilbert's primitive terms for plane geometry were "point," "line," "on," "between," "congruent"; and his postulates were arranged in five groups: I. Postulates of Connection (those concerned with incidence), II. Postulates of Order, III. Postulates of Congruence, IV. Postulates of Parallels, V. Postulates of Continuity.

If one begins by assuming all of these postulates and then suppresses certain of them, keeping at each stage only those theorems that follow from the retained postulates, he generates a whole new series of geometries (which might be called *modified* Euclidean geometries). For example, if the Postulate of Parallels of Euclidean geometry is dropped (and not replaced by some other postulate concerned with parallels which would thereby give a form of non–Euclidean geometry), one obtains what Bolyai called *absolute* geometry.[‡] If we drop all of the postulates of groups II, III, IV, and V and retain only the postulates relating to incidence, it is natural to call the resulting geometry *incidence* geometry.[§]

Although we shall not reproduce any of them, many different sets of postulates for projective geometry have been devised. They all have in common some postulates on incidence. Thus from the point of view of Klein, one should probably classify incidence geometry as intermediate between topology and projective geometry.

[†] See Hilbert *35*, or Eves *22*, pp. 443–45.

[‡] See Coxeter *19*, pp. 175, 263–87, or Blumenthal *12*, p. 53.

[§] See Moise *49*, Chap. 2. In *Basic Concepts of Geometry* (New York: Blaisdell Publishing Company, 1965), published while this book was in proof, Walter Prenowitz and Meyer Jordan use the concept of incidence geometry "as a basic unifying idea."

Instead of using *Incidence Geometry* as a title, however, we have preferred to use *The Geometry of Incidence*, thus indicating that we shall stress some of those portions of such geometries as projective and affine that appear to depend only, or primarily, on the postulates of incidence. " The theorems relating to incidence are by far the most important theorems of projective geometry."[†]

After this rather lengthy digression, we now return to the program outlined in the final paragraph of Section 1.1.

1.3   *Ideal Elements*

One of the most important ideas in mathematics is that of one-to-one correspondence. Whenever an association can be shown to exist between the members of two sets of elements in such a manner that each element of the first set is associated with exactly one element of the second, and vice versa, then this association, or *pairing*, of the members of the two sets is called a *one-to-one correspondence*.

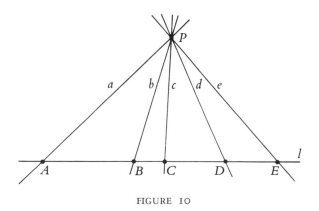

FIGURE 10

---

† Hilbert and Cohn-Vossen *36*, p. 95.

In Figure 10, we have two sets of different kinds of elements.†
One set consists of points such as *A, B, C,* ... ‡ that lie on the line
l, the so-called *point row* or *pencil of points* l (*A, B, C,* ...). The other
set consists of lines such as *a, b, c,* ... that pass through the point *P*
(which does not lie on the line *l*). This second set is usually called a
flat pencil or a *pencil of lines* and is denoted by *P* (*a, b, c,* ...). The
incidence of point *A* with line *a*, of point *B* with line *b*, etc.,
affords a visual association between the members of the point row
on *l* and the flat pencil at *P*. Is this a one-to-one correspondence?

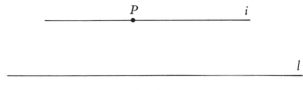

FIGURE 11

At first sight it looks as if the answer is yes. Although there are
infinitely many points on *l*, and infinitely many lines through *P*,
apparently we could draw a line through *every* point of *l* and
through *P* and thus set up the correspondence in that direction.
But we still have the "vice versa" part of the definition to be
checked. Does *every* line through *P* correspond to a point on *l*?
At once we see that the line *i* through *P* (Figure 11) which is
parallel to *l* has no mate or corresponding point on *l*, and our
correspondence fails to be one-to-one. That is, more precisely, *i*
has no mate on *l* when our realm of discussion is the Euclidean
plane where parallel lines do not meet.

Once again we have come up against an awkward special

---

† We shall consistently label points with capital letters and lines with lower
case letters.

‡ The three dots " ... " mean " and so forth."

case caused by parallel lines. Is there anything we can do about it?

Curiously enough it was probably the work of certain Renaissance painters, such as Alberti, Leonardo, and Dürer,[†] that suggested a concept to the great German astronomer Johann Kepler (1571–1630) which later became one of the key ideas in the development of the new geometry that we are going to study. These painters observed that in order to make two-dimensional drawings that would actually portray three-dimensional scenes, they had to draw parallel lines as if they met at a so-called vanishing point on the horizon. To illustrate this idea in a very simple case, Figure 12 is supposed to represent a railroad track crossing a desert.

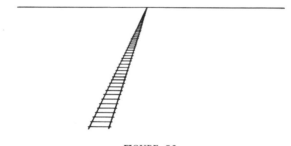

FIGURE 12

Since we lacked only *one* point on the Euclidean line *l* of Figure 10 in order to set up a one-to-one correspondence between the point row on *l* and the flat pencil at *P*, why not, with the artist's vanishing point in mind, *create* an additional point *I* on *l*? We could then think of the new line as an extension of our Euclidean line *l* with *A*, *B*, *C*, ... being considered ordinary points and *I* as some kind of *extra*ordinary point on this line.

[†] See Kline *42*, Chap. X, or Coxeter *19*, p. 229, or Ivins *37*, Chaps. V, VI, VII.

Visually, of course, we are unhappy about this. Unlike the Renaissance artists, we can travel in a third dimension. To a person flying above the desert, the railway track would look something like Figure 13, i.e. the rails would appear to have *two* vanishing points. However we want only one extraordinary point on our extended line. On which end of the line shall we put

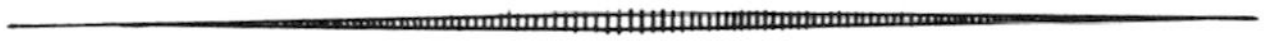

FIGURE 13

it? And incidentally, just where is this point to be located? We permit the artist by some kind of artistic license to draw a point that we know does not exist, but we are not so willing to grant this privilege to the geometer.

To say that the point is at infinity may appear to some readers to be the solution. Historically this is what was done, and the new point was called the point at infinity. This terminology, however, paves the way for all kinds of irrelevant philosophical discussions. Hence, in self defense, most geometers have preferred to call the added point an *ideal* point. There are many dictionary meanings for the adjective ideal, but perhaps the person who first applied *ideal* to our *extra*ordinary point had in mind the meaning "existing as a mere mental image; existing in fancy or imagination only." This was back in the days when, following Euclid, an ordinary point was still defined in the dictionary as "that which has neither parts nor extent, but position only." Thus ordinary points—represented on paper by dots—were pretty shadowy things, but at least *they* had position or location.

It is certainly a far cry from the definition given above to the one that is found in the Second Edition of Webster's New International Dictionary, first copyrighted in 1934, and in others based on this work. Here the relevant definition is: " *Math*. An undefined geometric element concerning which it is postulated that at least two exist and that two suffice to determine a line." The extreme caution of part of this statement, i.e. where it is " postulated that at least two [points] exist," should be enough to persuade anyone acquainted with mathematicians that this was written by one of them.

The statement does in fact describe accurately the present-day status of ordinary points in synthetic geometry. They are regarded simply as undefined geometric elements concerning which we assume only that two of them are sufficient for the determination of a line (which may or may not also be considered to be an undefined element in geometry. More about this later). Thus the statement describing Figure 1 at the beginning of the book assumes considerable importance. As indicated at the end of the last section, it is one of the foundation stones on which Euclidean and other geometries rest, and we shall return to a discussion of it later. For the present we shall merely say that if the reader is disturbed by this new interpretation or meaning of " point," we assure him that most of the time we shall continue to represent ordinary points by dots on the paper. But how about a representation for our extraordinary or ideal points? So far, all that we have found it necessary to assume about these is that there is to be only one of them on, or incident with, a given line.

Let us consider a horizontal line *l*. An ordinary point on *l* is indicated by a dot and is designated by a capital letter such as *A*. Presumably we could represent the ideal point on *l* by any other capital letter such as *B*, but the big problem is the location for *B*. No matter where we place *B* on *l* there will be the danger of confusing this ideal point *B* with some ordinary point in its vicinity (possibly under the assumption that the printer forgot to include a dot for *B*). To avoid this possible confusion, we shall use capital letters with asterisks to represent ideal points, e.g. *B**, and usually we shall place this letter near an edge of the figure (Figure 14). For the horizontal line *l*, it makes no difference, of course, whether we place this representation at the right- or left-hand edge.

FIGURE 14

Next, suppose we add to Figure 14 a vertical line *m* through the ordinary point *A* and call its ideal point *C** (Figure 15). What is it that enables us to distinguish between *B** and *C** ? It is, of course, the directions of *l* and *m* (horizontal or east-west and vertical or north-south, respectively), where by direction we are not thinking of the two senses or orders by which we might traverse one of the lines, e.g. from left to right (west to east) or from right to left (east to west) on *l*.

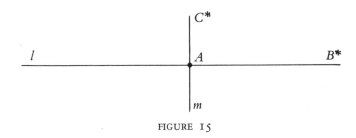

FIGURE 15

An ideal point, then, is indicated by a direction, or by the direction of a straight line (assuming for the time being that we have some idea of what we mean by a straight line, i.e. the representation of an ordinary straight line in the Euclidean plane is the mark made on the paper by tracing along something called a straight edge), where we assume that the straight line has one (i.e. a unique) direction.

Now what about two parallel lines, say two horizontal lines? Each line is to have one ideal point. Are these ideal points to be regarded as distinct? If so, we would have trouble in distinguishing between them since we would certainly want to say that two horizontal lines have the same direction. About now, also, we recall our description of Figure 2, in which we said, "Exactly one point lies on, or is incident with, every two distinct lines (unless the lines are parallel)," and our objective of trying to remove special cases caused by parallel lines. Certainly then we have ample motivation for saying that we shall add only one ideal point for each family of parallel lines, i.e. that all members of a family of parallel lines are incident with the same (unique) ideal point. We shall, of course, want to say that different families of parallels are incident with different ideal points.

As we have now conceived of these new ideal points, do they satisfy the present-day fundamental assumption concerning points, namely that two points suffice to determine a line? If we consider first one ordinary point and one ideal point, it is evident that an ordinary line is determined, i.e. a line through the ordinary point with the direction given by the ideal point.

But what if we start with two distinct ideal points? Certainly they will not determine what we have called an ordinary line since such lines contain only one ideal point. Thus we are forced by logic to create a new type of line which we shall naturally call an *ideal line*—one that is determined by two distinct ideal points. Does such an ideal line contain any ordinary points? No, because an ordinary point and one ideal point determine an ordinary line.

How many ideal lines must we create? *One* will be sufficient for plane geometry if we assume that it contains *all* the ideal points. As the reader has probably guessed, in addition to removing the awkward special case in the description of Figure 2, we would like if possible to have this statement hold for *all* lines, ordinary or ideal. Thus we would like to have an ideal line have a unique point in common with *every* ordinary line. This will happen only if these points in common are ideal and if they all lie on a unique ideal line. We therefore have no need for more than one new, extraordinary or ideal line to be added to the Euclidean plane. This corresponds to our adding only one ideal point to an ordinary Euclidean line to obtain an extended Euclidean line.

The reader should now take a new look at the figures in Section 1.1. In the extended Euclidean plane (which is the same as the affine plane if we ignore the concepts of distance and perpendicularity), Figure 2(b) represents two distinct lines that are incident with the same (ideal) point. Figure 4(c) represents a triangle (with one ideal vertex), and Figure 4(d), three lines concurrent at the same (ideal) point.

Needless to say, complete acceptance of ideal elements comes only with their continued use. We shall conclude this section by linking ideal points and central projection in a manner that may be reassuring to the reader.

In Figure 16 we have a point row l_1 $(A_1, B_1, C_1, \ldots)$ projected by means of a central projection with center at P onto a second point row l_2 $(A_2, B_2, C_2, \ldots)$, or vice versa. The mate of any point on l_1 such as C_1 is found by constructing a line through this point and P and then locating the point C_2 which is the intersection of the constructed line with l_2. Evidently, the point of l_1, D_1, which also lies on l_2 must correspond to itself, i.e. D_1 and D_2 are different labels for the same point (called a *self-corresponding* point).

Under the above central projection, to what point on l_2 does the ideal point, I_1^*, on l_1 correspond? We follow the same construction as before; only this time it looks different. Drawing

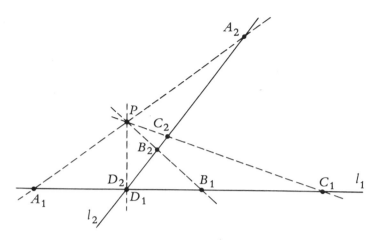

FIGURE 16

a line through P and I_1^* means, of course, drawing a line through P which is parallel to l_1. For our figure, such a line evidently has an ordinary point, I_2, in common with l_2 (Figure 17). Thus we have shown that an ideal point on one line may be projected by a central projection into an ordinary point on a second line. The reader should have no difficulty in locating the ordinary point on l_1 that corresponds to the ideal point on l_2.

Although we ignore ideal elements in the next section, we shall return to them in the following section.

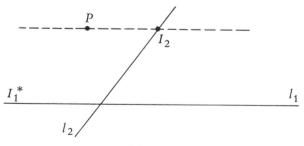

FIGURE 17

We can summarize Section 1.3 as follows: The extended Euclidean plane is formed by adding one *extra*ordinary or ideal point for each family of parallel lines (independent of the two senses along any member of the family), with the totality of new points regarded as an ideal line which contains no ordinary points. In this extended plane two distinct points (ordinary or ideal) always determine one line, and two distinct lines (one of which may by the ideal line) always intersect in one point (ordinary or ideal). The affine plane is merely the extended Euclidean plane without the concepts of perpendicularity and distance having been defined.

1.4 Line Curves and Line Coordinates

In analytic geometry we think of a curve or locus as made up of the set of points whose coordinates (ordered pairs of real numbers) satisfy the equation of the curve. We know that except in unusual cases—as for example in $x^2 + y^2 = 0$, where $(0, 0)$ is the only point whose coordinates satisfy the equation—we must be content with identifying only a few among infinitely many of these points. Hence we are satisfied by plotting strategically located points and then drawing as smooth a curve as possible through these points.

If we have the equations of two curves that intersect, the coordinates of the common points can be found if we solve the equations simultaneously. For example, the coordinates of the points of intersection of the circle with equation $x^2 + y^2 = 25$ and the hyperbola with equation $x^2 - y^2 = 7$ are quickly found[†] to be $(4, 3)$, $(4, -3)$, $(-4, 3)$, $(-4, -3)$ (see Figure 18).

[†] Although this discussion proceeds as if the reader is familiar with the techniques of analytic geometry and algebra, actually it is not necessary to understand all of the details in order to get the gist of the ideas that are being discussed.

In plane Euclidean geometry, the tangent to a circle is defined as the line that has exactly one point in common with the circle. This same definition can be used for the other curves whose equations are of second degree, i.e. for the ellipses, parabolas, and hyperbolas.

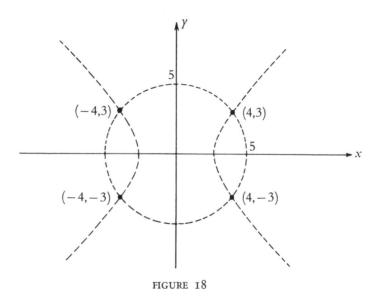

FIGURE 18

Two such curves may or may not have some common tangents, i.e. lines that are tangent to each curve. A hasty sketch of the parabola with equation $2y^2 = x$ and the ellipse with equation $5x^2 + 20y^2 = 4$ indicates that these curves apparently have two common tangents (Figure 19). Finding the equations of these common tangents appears to be a relatively simple problem, but it usually taxes the abilities of the better college students even after they have available the resources of the differential calculus.

As we have indicated in an earlier paragraph, analytic geometry has been developed by taking the point as the element or funda-mental building block. Curves, including straight lines, are then considered to be collections of these points whose coordinates satisfy certain equations. On the other hand, in Euclidean synthetic

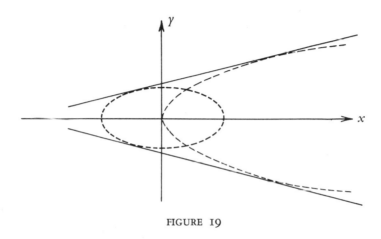

geometry, both points and lines are taken as undefined elements, and—as we have seen in Section I.3—points and lines can have equal billing in the extended Euclidean plane. What, if any-thing, can be done about defining curves in terms of lines?

Consider the locus of all lines that can be drawn in the plane at a constant (perpendicular) distance from some fixed point (Figure 20). Although we have drawn only a small number of these lines, the polygon made up of pieces of these lines is a crude approximation to the curve we have already called a circle. By drawing more lines, we get a better approximation. The idealized situation is shown in Figure 21, where the black area indicates portions of so many lines that the white page does not show between them.

We can now think of the circle as being defined by the set of

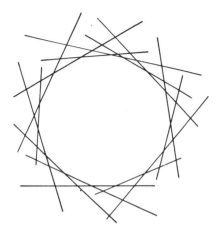

FIGURE 20

FIGURE 21

its tangent lines. This leads to the concept of a line locus in addition to the one that we already have of a point locus. The "line circle" is evidently related to the "point circle" by an incidence relationship, i.e. the lines are those that are each incident with one and only one point of the point locus, and the points are those that are each incident with one and only one line of the line locus.

If we can now introduce *line coordinates* in such a way that a line locus consists of those lines which satisfy an equation in line coordinates, then our problem of finding the common tangents to the given parabola and ellipse will be analogous to the one we solved earlier when we found the common points for the given circle and hyperbola. That is, to find the common tangents, we shall merely solve simultaneously the line equations of the parabola and ellipse. Our initial approach to those coordinates will not be entirely satisfactory, but later sections will supply more generality and will make clearer the fundamental nature of the line as an element in plane projective geometry.

The general equation in point coordinates of the straight line in the xy-plane is

$$(\text{I.I}) \qquad\qquad Ax + By + C = 0,$$

where A, B, and C are constants. If $C \neq 0$, the line does not pass through the origin since $(0, 0)$ does not satisfy (I.I) in that case. For such lines, we can divide each term in the equation by C, obtaining

$$(\text{I.2}) \qquad\qquad (A/C)x + (B/C)y + 1 = 0.$$

We now set $A/C = u$ and $B/C = v$, and hence (I.2) becomes

$$(\text{I.3}) \qquad\qquad ux + vy + 1 = 0.$$

Next, we look for geometric interpretations for u and v. In analytic geometry, it is customary to identify the point where a non-vertical line (i.e. one for which $A \neq 0$) intersects the x-axis by giving it the coordinates $(a, 0)$, where a is called the x-intercept of the line. Since the equation of the x-axis is $y = 0$, we evidently find the x-intercept for the line given by Equation (1.1) by substituting zero for y and solving for x. Thus $a = -C/A$. In similar fashion, for a non-vertical line we find $b = -C/B$. Comparing these with the expressions for u and v, we have now shown that u and v in Equation (1.3) represent the negative reciprocals of the intercepts of the line given by this equation on the x- and y-axes respectively.

A simple illustration may be helpful. For the straight line with equation $2x + 3y - 6 = 0$, we first divide all terms by -6, obtaining

$$-\tfrac{1}{3}x - \tfrac{1}{2}y + 1 = 0,$$

and observe that since $u = -\tfrac{1}{3}$, $v = -\tfrac{1}{2}$, then $a = 3$, $b = 2$. The student of analytic geometry sees nothing new thus far. It is standard operating procedure to construct the graphs of lines not passing through the origin by finding the intercepts on the co-ordinate axes. A longer procedure would be to first solve for y in terms of x,

$$3y = 6 - 2x,$$
$$y = (6 - 2x)/3,$$

then give values to x and compute the corresponding values of y to find the coordinates of other points on the line, e.g. when $x = 1$, $y = \tfrac{4}{3}$; when $x = 2$, $y = \tfrac{2}{3}$, etc. Such results are usually written in the following tabular form:

x	1	2	-1	...
y	$\tfrac{4}{3}$	$\tfrac{2}{3}$	$\tfrac{8}{3}$	...

The common property that these points possess is, of course, that they are all incident with the same line (the line whose

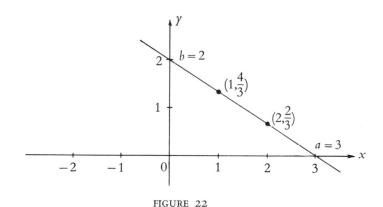

FIGURE 22

equation is $2x + 3y - 6 = 0$) when the point is used as the fundamental element (Figure 22).

Now suppose that in Equation (1.3) we think of x and y as constants, say $x = 3$ and $y = -2$, and ask what the corresponding equation

$$3u - 2v + 1 = 0$$

represents. The answer is probably obvious, but we shall proceed as if this were not the case. Following the "longer procedure" of the preceding paragraph, we can solve for v in terms of u, obtaining

$$-2v = -1 - 3u,$$
$$v = (1 + 3u)/2.$$

We now give values to u and calculate the corresponding values of v.

u	1	-1	$\frac{1}{3}$	...
v	2	-1	1	...

Our preceding example suggests to us that to each ordered pair of numbers for u and v there corresponds a straight line. We now

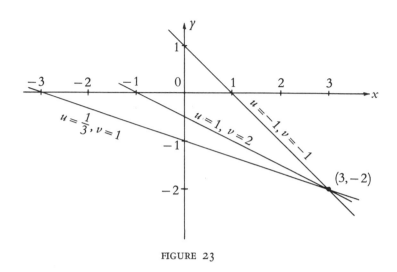

FIGURE 23

construct some of these lines and ask what property they have in common (Figure 23). The common property is that they all pass through the point $(3, -2)$. This is the answer that was probably obvious when we asked the question about the representation of the equation $3u - 2v + 1 = 0$, since in forming this equation we introduced $x = 3, y = -2$.

It should now be quite natural to say that the line with equation $-\frac{1}{3}x - \frac{1}{2}y + 1 = 0$ in point coordinates also has $u = -\frac{1}{3}$ and $v = -\frac{1}{2}$ as *line coordinates*—which we shall write as $[-\frac{1}{3}, -\frac{1}{2}]$ to avoid confusion with point coordinates—and that the point $(3, -2)$ in point coordinates has the *equation* $3u - 2v + 1 = 0$ in line coordinates.

Before making a general statement about line coordinates, it will be well to look at several special cases. Remembering that $u = -1/a$ (or $a = -1/u$), we see that as u approaches zero, a becomes infinite. This means that for $v \neq 0$ (so that b is finite), as u approaches zero, the corresponding line approaches parallelism with the x-axis. Thus we can say that horizontal lines (other than the x-axis) are represented by $u = 0$ with $v \neq 0$. In like manner, $v = 0$ with $u \neq 0$ will represent vertical lines (other than the y-axis). Thus we can say that all ordered pairs of real numbers for u and v, with the exception of the pair given when both $u = 0$ and $v = 0$, represent ordinary lines in the plane. Conversely, all ordinary lines of the plane except those passing through the origin can be represented by ordered pairs of real numbers for u and v. Following J. Plücker (1801–68), we define $[u, v]$ as the *line co-ordinates* of such lines. The equation $ux + vy + 1 = 0$ with x and y held constant (but not both equal to zero) can be thought of as the *line equation* of the point (x, y). This equation, expressing the incidence of point and line, is referred to as the incidence relation or the equation of united position of point and line. The cases excluded, e.g. lines through the origin and $u = 0$, $v = 0$ simultaneously, will be treated in the next section.

We now proceed to find the equation in line coordinates of a line curve which consists of the tangent lines to a point curve with a given equation in point coordinates, for example, the parabola $2y^2 = x$. With u and v held constant, $ux + vy + 1 = 0$ is the equation of a line in point coordinates. When we solve this equation simultaneously with the equation of the parabola, we find the coordinates of the points of intersection. Thus, substituting the expression for x from the equation of the parabola into the equation of the line, we obtain

$$2uy^2 + vy + 1 = 0$$

as a quadratic equation in y whose two roots, if they are distinct real numbers, will be the ordinates of the two points of intersection of the line and parabola. We want the two points of intersection to come together to produce a tangent line to the parabola. Algebraically this will happen if and only if the discriminant of the quadratic equation ($B^2 - 4AC$ for the general quadratic in y, $Ay^2 + By + C = 0$) is equal to zero. Calculating this discriminant for our equation and equating it to zero, we find

$$v^2 - 8u = 0$$

as the condition in u and v that must be satisfied by the line coordinates $[u, v]$ of the tangent lines to the parabola whose point equation is $2y^2 = x$. Quite naturally, we call $v^2 - 8u = 0$ the line equation of the parabola.

Likewise, we find the line equation of the ellipse of our earlier problem to be $4u^2 + v^2 = 5$. The simultaneous solution of this equation with $v^2 - 8u = 0$ yields $[\frac{1}{2}, \pm 2]$ as the line coordinates of the common tangents. Hence in point coordinates the equations of these tangent lines are $\frac{1}{2}x \pm 2y + 1 = 0$, or $x \pm 4y + 2 = 0$.

The problem we have solved is only one of many whose solution is expedited by the use of line coordinates.[10] The English mathematician J. J. Sylvester (1814–97) has paid tribute to Plücker, the inventor of line coordinates, in the following words:

> *Until these recent times, the analytic method of geometry, as given by Descartes, has been suffered to go on halting as it were on one foot. To Plücker was reserved the honor of setting it firmly on its two equal supports by supplying the complementary system of coordinates.*[†]

1.5   *Homogeneous Coordinates*

We begin this section by considering the so-called real number line. First we select a point O, called the origin, on, say, a horizontal line, to represent the number zero, and another point U, called the unit point, to the right of O to represent the number one. This choice determines the uniform scale. Next, we assume that

---

† Quoted in Winger 70, p. 15.

to every other point on the line there corresponds in the scale exactly one real number, and, conversely, to every real number in the scale there corresponds exactly one point on the line. Thus the real number line is illustrated by the familiar x-axis of plane analytic geometry, where, for any general point P on this line, we call the corresponding real number x the x-coordinate of the point (Figure 24).

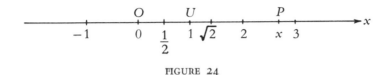

FIGURE 24

So far we have talked only about an ordinary line. If we now want to add an ideal point to the line, what coordinate shall we assign to the ideal point, say I^*? We would like it to be a real number, since all of the ordinary points of the line have real coordinates, but unfortunately we have already exhausted the supply of real numbers in the process of labeling the ordinary points. Recalling that historically an ideal point was regarded as a point at infinity, there is a temptation to use the symbol ∞ as a coordinate for the ideal point. This is highly unsatisfactory for several reasons. Although mathematicians sometimes use ∞ as an abbreviation for a longer statement that describes the situation when a variable or a function becomes infinite, ∞ is *not* a symbol for a real number. Thus

$$\lim_{x \to 0} 1/x = \infty$$

should be read, " $1/x$ *becomes infinite* as x approaches zero " rather than " the limit *equals* infinity," or " the limit *is* infinity."

Even if it were possible to treat ∞ as a number, there would still be the awkward choice of a plus or minus sign to precede it.

Remember that there is to be only *one* ideal point on a line, and we do not want to imply that it lies either to the right or to the left.

To extricate themselves from this difficulty, mathematicians have used an ingenious device that at first sight appears to be a step backwards, i.e. one that appears to further complicate the situation. Instead of *one* coordinate to locate a point on the extended line, they use *two* numbers !

Their reasoning goes something as follows. Suppose we set $x = \bar{x}/\bar{z}$ and use the ordered pair $(\bar{x}, \bar{z})$—read x bar, z bar—to represent the point formerly represented by x.[†] When $\bar{z} = 1$, then $\bar{x} = x$ and $(x, 1)$, for all real numbers x, is the new (and apparently more complicated) representation for the ordinary points formerly denoted by x. For $\bar{x} = 0$, but with $\bar{z} \neq 0$, $x = 0$ (since the quotient of zero by any real number not zero is defined to be zero). Here is a new difficulty. We now have infinitely many representations for our point O, i.e. $(0, 7)$, $(0, -13)$, $(0, \pi)$, etc., all represent the same point. A similar situation is encountered when we consider representations for the point U, formerly denoted by 1. These will occur for $\bar{x} = \bar{z}$. Hence $(5, 5)$, $(\frac{1}{2}, \frac{1}{2})$, $(-1, -1)$, etc., all represent U. In fact, we have this difficulty all along the line since, for example, $(2, 3)$, $(4, 6)$, $(-6, -9)$, etc., all correspond to $x = \frac{2}{3}$.

On the credit side of the ledger, however, there is a great gain. Such pairs as $(113, 0)$, $(-4, 0)$, etc., do *not* represent ordinary points since these would require the x-representation to be written with a zero in the denominator, and division by zero is an inadmissible operation in mathematics. Here, then, is something we can use for the ideal point, but once again there are infinitely many such representations.

[†] $\bar{z}$ is not to be confused with the z-coordinate used in three-dimensional analytic geometry.

The price we shall have to pay to make our new representation *unique* for each point (including the ideal point) is evidently to regard $(\bar{x}, \bar{z})$ and $(k\bar{x}, k\bar{z})$, where k is any real number different from zero, as equivalent representations for the same point P. At first this may appear to be a high price, but one soon becomes accustomed to it. As a matter of fact, we can now avoid the use of fractions. The point $(\frac{2}{3}, \frac{5}{7})$, which in the old notation is

$$x = \frac{2/3}{5/7} \cdot \frac{21}{21} = \frac{14}{15},$$

can now be written as $(14, 15)$, obtainable directly by taking $k = 21$. Likewise the point $(60, 25)$ can be written in the simpler form $(12, 5)$ by taking $k = \frac{1}{5}$. Evidently the most convenient form for O is $(0, 1)$, for U is $(1, 1)$ and for I^* is $(1, 0)$. As the reader may guess, these points will have special significance later.

One pair of numbers with a unique form has so far not been mentioned in our discussion. This pair is $(0, 0)$, and corresponds in the x-notation to the indeterminate form $0/0$. Fortunately we have no need for this pair, so we simply agree that $(0, 0)$ is undefined or meaningless in the $\bar{x}\bar{z}$-notation.

We have gone into considerable detail in showing how the ideal point of the x-axis can be coordinatized. If the reader clearly understands what we have done so far, he will have no difficulty in seeing how this idea can be extended to the xy-plane of analytic geometry. In addition to placing $x = \bar{x}/\bar{z}$, we also place $y = \bar{y}/\bar{z}$ and use the ordered triple $(\bar{x}, \bar{y}, \bar{z})$ to replace the ordered pair of coordinates (x, y). We must now agree not to use the zero triple $(0, 0, 0)$, and to treat $(\bar{x}, \bar{y}, \bar{z})$ and $(k\bar{x}, k\bar{y}, k\bar{z})$, for $k \neq 0$, as equivalent representations for the same point. Convenient representations for special points in the xy-plane are as follows: $(0, 0, 1)$ for the origin, $(1, 0, 0)$ for the ideal point on the x-axis, $(0, 1, 0)$ for the ideal point on the y-axis, and $(1, 1, 1)$ for the unit point, i.e. for the point $(1, 1)$ in ordinary coordinates.

When the point is used as the element in analytic geometry, lines are characterized as those sub-sets of the plane whose coordinates satisfy first-degree equations in x and y. Thus $y = 0$ describes all points on the x-axis and is called the equation of the x-axis. In our new representation, $\bar{y} = 0$ is the equation of the x-axis, $\bar{x} = 0$ is the equation of the y-axis, and $\bar{z} = 0$ will be the equation of the ideal line of the xy-plane. The general equation of the straight line, $Ax + By + C = 0$, will become $A\bar{x} + B\bar{y} + C\bar{z} = 0$ when we replace x by $\bar{x}/\bar{z}$ and y by $\bar{y}/\bar{z}$ and multiply through by $\bar{z}$ (assumed different from zero for ordinary lines). We now have what is called a homogeneous equation of first degree in $\bar{x}$, $\bar{y}$, $\bar{z}$. For our purposes, this simply means that all terms of the equation are of the same (first) degree in the three variables $\bar{x}$, $\bar{y}$, or $\bar{z}$. Having reached this stage, it will be appropriate to call $\bar{x}$, $\bar{y}$, $\bar{z}$ homogeneous coordinates in the plane and to refer to x, y as non-homogeneous coordinates. ($Ax + By + C = 0$ is, of course, a non-homogeneous equation.)

To obtain homogeneous point *and* line coordinates and equations, we could replace the u and v of Section 1.4 by $\bar{u}/\bar{w}$ and $\bar{v}/\bar{w}$ respectively, and after multiplying by $\bar{w}$, our incidence relationship would become

$$\bar{u}\bar{x} + \bar{v}\bar{y} + \bar{w}\bar{z} = 0.$$

The exceptional cases that we encountered in the nonhomogeneous form no longer cause trouble, e.g. lines through the origin are given by $\bar{u}\bar{x} + \bar{v}\bar{y} = 0$.

These new coordinates and equations could be applied to the subject matter of ordinary plane analytic geometry—or Cartesian geometry as it is sometimes called—to give us the analytic geometry of the extended Cartesian plane. Actually such an analytic geometry serves as a model[11] or interpretation for the geometry of the affine plane, where the ideal line plays a role

different from the other lines of the plane but where perpendicularity and distance are not defined.

In plane projective geometry—where we do not have the concept of parallelism—the ideal line is to be indistinguishable from
the other lines of the plane. The immediate reaction of most
readers to this statement is probably that such a situation is impossible. It was bad enough to extend the Euclidean plane by adding
the ideal line containing the ideal points, but now to make this
line indistinguishable from the ordinary lines of the plane appears
to be going too far! Indeed, it is impossible to visualize the projective plane in the ordinary manner. We shall give some satisfactory visual models of the real projective plane later, but what
are called points and lines in these models will bear little resemblance to our previous pictures for points and lines. When we use
the algebraic approach—as we shall do in the next chapter—this
difficulty simply does not arise.

We have tried to pave the way for such an approach, but we
warn the reader that it is going to be a matter of making a fresh
start. To emphasize this, we shall use new notation. Thus warned,
the reader should be in the proper state of mind to begin Chapter
II. If, however, the thought of leaving all familiar pictures behind
is too upsetting, we close this chapter by repeating an earlier statement to the effect that, assuming ordinary algebra, for the theorems
of projective geometry we can always have an affine interpretation and construct a picture in the extended Cartesian plane.

Although modern mathematics has de-emphasized the use of
pictures, there are still good reasons for having them. We quote
Jenner:

> *Finally, to put the matter of pictorial representation in its proper per-*
> *spective, there seem to be at least two reasons for its importance. In the*
> *first place, there is no doubt that pictures of curves and other geometric ob-*
> *jects are suggestive of appropriate geometric ideas which often generalize*

to the case of arbitrary fields. The second reason is much less austere but is, nevertheless, nothing to be ashamed of. This is the undeniable fact that the pictures are interesting and pleasant just to look at. The purpose of algebra definitely is not to take all the joy out of life.[†]

---

† Jenner *39*, p. 26.

II

The Real
Projective Plane

II.1   The Real Projective Plane Defined

In this chapter we shall discuss only the analytic geometry of the real projective plane, although later we shall see that there exist more general projective planes. We shall be concerned with ordered triples of real numbers other than the zero triple 0, 0, 0. When we enclose the triple in parentheses, the notation x_1, x_2, x_3 will be used and (x_1, x_2, x_3) will be called a *point*.[†] When the

---

[†] Humpty Dumpty would not have been bothered by this.
"*When* I *use a word,*" *Humpty Dumpty said in rather a scornful tone,* " *it means just what I choose it to mean—neither more nor less.*"
"*The question is,*" *said Alice,* "*whether you* can *make words mean so many different things.*"
"*The question is,*" *said Humpty Dumpty,*" "*which is to be master—that's all.*"
From *Through the Looking-glass* by the mathematician C. L. Dodgson, under the pseudonym Lewis Carroll.[12]

triple is enclosed in brackets, then u_1, u_2, u_3 will be used for the representative element and $[u_1, u_2, u_3]$ will be called a *line*. Point (x_1, x_2, x_3) will be defined to be incident with line $[u_1, u_2, u_3]$, and vice versa, if and only if

$$(\text{II.1}) \qquad\qquad u_1x_1 + u_2x_2 + u_3x_3 = 0.$$

Furthermore, (x_1, x_2, x_3) and (kx_1, kx_2, kx_3), for all non-zero constants k, will be said to be equivalent representations for the same point. This will be indicated by the notation $(x_1, x_2, x_3) \sim (kx_1, kx_2, kx_3)$.[13] Likewise for $[u_1, u_2, u_3]$ and $[ku_1, ku_2, ku_3]$. Equation (II.1), with u_1, u_2, u_3 considered constant, will be called the equation of the line $[u_1, u_2, u_3]$. Likewise, with the x's considered constant, (II.1) will be called the equation of the point (x_1, x_2, x_3).

We now have a formulation for the *real projective plane*, or, as it is sometimes called, the *projective plane over the real numbers*. The analytic projective geometry† that we are going to do in this chapter is sometimes called *pure* projective geometry in order to distinguish it from the synthetic projective geometry that is developed from a set of postulates in which points and lines are among the undefined or primitive concepts.

In the past, the order of presentation for projective geometry has frequently been to use the synthetic method first to build up a considerable body of theorems. Then when a point of diminishing returns is reached, the more powerful algebraic method is introduced—much as is the case when ordinary Euclidean geometry is followed by ordinary analytic geometry. For the real projective plane, in addition to postulates concerned with incidence, it is found necessary to introduce postulates concerned with order and continuity. More general projective geometries

---

† See Heyting *34*, section 1.4.

may not require all of these postulates, but they may require certain others that frequently appear unusual or artificial to the beginner.

A different approach that has many advantages is to start as we have just done by defining a point in the plane to be an ordered triple (x_1, x_2, x_3).[†] If the x's can be any real numbers—as we have assumed—then we shall be led to real projective plane geometry. By permitting the x's to be complex numbers for example, we define the complex projective plane. Other choices for the x's will lead to finite projective planes, etc. In similar fashion, a point in a space of three dimensions can be defined as (x_1, x_2, x_3, x_4), and the procedure for the extension to n dimensions now becomes apparent.[‡] Moreover, the algebraic formulation gives a model for corresponding postulational systems, a model that can be used to give what are called consistency proofs[§] for the postulates.

We shall illustrate this for what are essentially the only postulates needed for the most general kind of a projective plane.[††] These are:

P1 Exactly one line is incident with every two distinct points.

P2 Exactly one point is incident with every two distinct lines.

We first consider P2. Let two distinct lines be given by $a = [a_1, a_2, a_3]$ and $b = [b_1, b_2, b_3]$. This means that the number triple a_1, a_2, a_3 is not proportional to the number triple b_1, b_2, b_3 and, of course, that neither of these is the zero triple. We now need

---

[†] See Veblen and Young *67*, p. 201.
[‡] See Schreier and Sperner *59*.
[§] See Eves *22*, p. 397.
[††] To be discussed in Chap. IV.

to exhibit the number triple for the unique point that is incident with both lines. This means that we must find a point $C = (c_1, c_2, c_3)$ satisfying the two incidence conditions

$$(\text{II.2}) \qquad \begin{aligned} a_1c_1 + a_2c_2 + a_3c_3 &= 0 \\ b_1c_1 + b_2c_2 + b_3c_3 &= 0, \end{aligned}$$

i.e. we must show that these two homogeneous linear equations have a simultaneous solution for c_1, c_2, c_3 which will represent a unique point.

Since the solution of this algebraic problem is going to be the key to much of our later development, it will be discussed in detail in the next few pages. Readers familiar with this material (and the dot- and cross-product notation of vector analysis) can give these pages the once-over-lightly treatment.

We begin by attempting to solve Equations (II.2) for c_1 and c_2 in terms of c_3, and hence rewrite these equations in the following form:

$$\begin{aligned} a_1c_1 + a_2c_2 &= -a_3c_3 \\ b_1c_1 + b_2c_2 &= -b_3c_3. \end{aligned}$$

If we now multiply each member of the first equation by b_2 and each member of the second equation by $- a_2$, they look as follows:

$$\begin{aligned} a_1b_2c_1 + a_2b_2c_2 &= -a_3b_2c_3 \\ -a_2b_1c_1 - a_2b_2c_2 &= a_2b_3c_3. \end{aligned}$$

By adding these equations, member for member, we obtain

$$a_1b_2c_1 - a_2b_1c_1 = -a_3b_2c_3 + a_2b_3c_3,$$

or $\qquad (a_1b_2 - a_2b_1)c_1 = (a_2b_3 - a_3b_2)c_3.$

Hence, if we can be certain that $a_1b_2 - a_2b_1 \neq 0$, we find

$$c_1 = \frac{a_2b_3 - a_3b_2}{a_1b_2 - a_2b_1}c_3.$$

Using a similar procedure to eliminate c_1 rather than c_2, we can also find

$$c_2 = \frac{a_3 b_1 - a_1 b_3}{a_1 b_2 - a_2 b_1} c_3.$$

Here again we must have $a_1 b_2 - a_2 b_1 \neq 0$. To justify such an assumption, we return to our hypothesis that $a = [a_1, a_2, a_3]$ and $b = [b_1, b_2, b_3]$ represented distinct lines and that hence the number triple a_1, a_2, a_3 is not proportional to the number triple b_1, b_2, b_3. If they were proportional, and $b_1, b_2,$ and b_3 are each non-zero, we would have

$$a_1/b_1 = a_2/b_2 = a_3/b_3.$$

In any case we would have

$$a_1 b_2 = a_2 b_1, a_1 b_3 = a_3 b_1, a_2 b_3 = a_3 b_2.$$

Hence if they are not proportional, at least one of the following statements must be true:

$$a_1 b_2 \neq a_2 b_1, a_1 b_3 \neq a_3 b_1, a_2 b_3 \neq a_3 b_2.$$

The first of these is of course equivalent to the condition we needed above, namely $a_1 b_2 - a_2 b_1 \neq 0$, and thus, if it is satisfied for our given lines, we are certain that we can solve for c_1 and c_2 in terms of c_3. If it were not satisfied, then either the second or third condition would have to be satisfied, and thus we could have solved for c_2 and c_3 in terms of c_1, or for c_1 and c_3 in terms of c_2. We have therefore established that under our hypothesis we would always be able to solve for two of the unknowns in terms of the third. The solution given can, therefore, be thought of as a representative solution for this situation.

To bring out the homogeneous nature of the solution, we now set

$$c_3 = k(a_1 b_2 - a_2 b_1),$$

and hence obtain

$$c_1 = k(a_2 b_3 - a_3 b_2)$$

and

$$c_2 = k(a_3 b_1 - a_1 b_3).$$

As far as algebra is concerned, $k = 0$ provides the *trivial solution* $c_1 = 0$, $c_2 = 0$, $c_3 = 0$, for the given pair of equations. In our work, we must discard this solution since $(0, 0, 0)$ has no meaning in the real projective plane. Thus we must have $k \neq 0$, and can write

$$(\text{II.3}) \quad (c_1, c_2, c_3) \sim (a_2 b_3 - a_3 b_2, a_3 b_1 - a_1 b_3, a_1 b_2 - a_2 b_1).$$

It so happens that expressions such as those in the left-hand sides of (II.1) and (II.3) appear very frequently in present-day mathematics. Concise notations have been introduced for them, and we may at times find it convenient to employ these notations. The expression

$$u_1 x_1 + u_2 x_2 + u_3 x_3,$$

i.e. the sum of the products of the u's and the x's, is called the *dot product* or the *inner product* of the ordered triples u_1, u_2, u_3 and x_1, x_2, x_3 and is written $u \cdot x$, i.e. by definition

$$(\text{II.4}) \qquad u \cdot x = u_1 x_1 + u_2 x_2 + u_3 x_3.$$

Using this notation, conditions (II.2) can now be written very concisely as

$$(\text{II.5}) \qquad \begin{aligned} a \cdot c &= 0 \\ b \cdot c &= 0 \end{aligned}$$

Ordinary multiplication of two real numbers is commutative, i.e. the order of the factors is immaterial, e.g. $3 \cdot 4 = 4 \cdot 3 = 12$. Evidently this new kind of multiplication for our triples of real numbers is also commutative since $u_1 x_1 + u_2 x_2 + u_3 x_3 = x_1 u_1 + x_2 u_2 + x_3 u_3$, i.e. $u \cdot x = x \cdot u$.

The *cross product* of two ordered triples a_1, a_2, a_3 and b_1, b_2, b_3, in that order is written $a \times b$ and is defined to be the ordered triple of the three numbers in the right-hand side of (II.3). i.e, by definition

(II.6) $a \times b = a_2b_3 - a_3b_2, a_3b_1 - a_1b_3, a_1b_2 - a_2b_1.$

For anyone who has not seen this definition before, it must appear to be a very queer one. So far we have given no clue as to its origin[14] but have merely stated that it will be useful. We now take a closer look at the definition. The fact that the order of a first and b second was specified in defining $a \times b$ probably leads us to suspect that this second kind of multiplication is not commutative, i.e. that in general $a \times b$ is not the same as $b \times a$.

The definition for $b \times a$ is logically obtained from the one for $a \times b$ by interchanging the a's and the b's thus

$$b \times a = b_2a_3 - b_3a_2, b_3a_1 - b_1a_3, b_1a_2 - b_2a_1.$$

Since the three expressions on the right are the negatives of the corresponding three in $a \times b$, we have $b \times a = -(a \times b)$, i.e. our cross multiplication is non-commutative.

In the interpretation of a number triple as a point or line however, the triple made up of the negatives of the numbers in a given triple is an equivalent representation for the point or line. For example, $(2, 3, -4) \sim (-2, -3, 4)$, where we have merely used $k = -1$ in the definition $(x_1, x_2, x_3) \sim (kx_1, kx_2, kx_3)$. In similar fashion $[-5, 6, -7] \sim [5, -6, 7]$. Hence we can say that $C \sim (a \times b)$ or $C \sim (b \times a)$, meaning by this that if we form the cross product (in either order) of the three members defining line a with those defining line b, we obtain a representation for the point C which is the unique point incident with a and b. From what we have said earlier, it is clear that if a and b are distinct lines, then the triple defining C can always be found and is never the zero triple. This means that exactly one point is always incident with every two distinct lines in the real projective plane.

The notation $C \sim (a \times b)$ is certainly compact but to apply it we need to remember (II.6). As a first step in obtaining a useful mnemonic device, we write the triples for a and b on two lines as follows:[15]

$$\begin{matrix} a_1 & a_2 & a_3 \\ b_1 & b_2 & b_3. \end{matrix}$$

With a second–order determinant

$$\begin{vmatrix} \alpha & \beta \\ \gamma & \delta \end{vmatrix}$$

defined as $\alpha\delta - \beta\gamma$, we see that the three expressions on the right-hand side in (II.6) can be thought of as three second-order determinants obtained from our two-row arrangement of the a's and b's above. The first two columns written as the determinant

$$\begin{vmatrix} a_1 & a_2 \\ b_1 & b_2 \end{vmatrix}$$

give the third term of (II.6), $a_1 b_2 - a_2 b_1$. Likewise, the determinant which is formed from the last two columns gives the first term, i.e.

$$\begin{vmatrix} a_2 & a_3 \\ b_2 & b_3 \end{vmatrix} = a_2 b_3 - a_3 b_2.$$

One might expect that the determinant formed from the first and third columns in the usual left-to-right order, i.e.

$$\begin{vmatrix} a_1 & a_3 \\ b_1 & b_3 \end{vmatrix} = a_1 b_3 - a_3 b_1,$$

would give the second term. Comparison with (II.6) shows that we have the negative of the expression we desire. If we could always remember to change the order of the columns for this determinant, we would have it, but there is a loss of symmetry here that is awkward. As a fresh start for obtaining something easier to remember, we not only write the a's and b's in two rows but repeat the first two columns of each. We then place below these letters three grouping symbols that will give our three determinants very simply with no changes in orders.

$$
\begin{array}{ccccc}
a_1 & a_2 & a_3 & a_1 & a_2 \\
b_1 & b_2 & b_3 & b_1 & b_2
\end{array}
$$

Thus we can now write

$$
(\text{II.7}) \qquad a \times b = \left(\begin{vmatrix} a_2 & a_3 \\ b_2 & b_3 \end{vmatrix}, \begin{vmatrix} a_3 & a_1 \\ b_3 & b_1 \end{vmatrix}, \begin{vmatrix} a_1 & a_2 \\ b_1 & b_2 \end{vmatrix} \right),
$$

where these three determinants are obtained as indicated above.

It is time for some examples. Let a be the line $[2, 3, -4]$ and b the line $[5, -1, 6]$. The point of intersection of these lines, $C = (c_1, c_2, c_3)$, is given by $a \times b$, and is calculated from

$$
\begin{array}{ccccc}
2 & 3 & -4 & 2 & 3 \\
5 & -1 & 6 & 5 & -1
\end{array}
$$

to be

$$
\left(\begin{vmatrix} 3 & -4 \\ -1 & 6 \end{vmatrix}, \begin{vmatrix} -4 & 2 \\ 6 & 5 \end{vmatrix}, \begin{vmatrix} 2 & 3 \\ 5 & -1 \end{vmatrix} \right)
$$

or

$$
(18 - 4, \, -20 - 12, \, -2 - 15) = (14, \, -32, \, -17).
$$

With a little practice, one writes the final result immediately after writing the arrangement of the number triples, that is, by calculating the values of the second-order determinants mentally without stopping to write them in explicit form.

We hope that this operation of calculating the cross product of two triples of numbers has appeared to be very easy to understand and to carry out. The pay-off is that almost all of the analytic projective geometry that we are going to do will consist merely of repeated use of this simple operation. But before we pursue this further, it will be instructive to consider the Cartesian model of what we have done in the preceding paragraph.

The equations for $a = [2, 3, -4]$ and $b = [5, -1, 6]$ in the projective plane are $2x_1 + 3x_2 - 4x_3 = 0$ and $5x_1 - x_2 + 6x_3 = 0$. By dividing through by x_3, and replacing x_1/x_3 by x and x_2/x_3 by y, we obtain $2x + 3y - 4 = 0$ and $5x - y + 6 = 0$ as the equations of the corresponding lines in our model. The simultaneous solution of these equations can be obtained by various methods, but a simple one is to multiply each term of the second equation by 3 and to add the members of the two equations ("If equals are added to equals, the sums are equal.") Thus:

$$
\begin{array}{r}
2x + 3y - 4 = 0 \\
15x - 3y + 18 = 0 \\
\hline
17x + 14 = 0
\end{array}
$$

Hence $x = -14/17$. Now we can substitute this value for x in either equation to find y, or else start all over again and this time eliminate x from the equations (for example by multiplying the first equation by 5 and the second by -2 before adding). The reader can check that $y = 32/17$.

Such a process as we have used for solving simultaneous, first-degree, non-homogeneous equations in x and y is not very difficult, but it is messy. Even when we choose integers for the coefficients of x and y and the constant term in the equations, fractions with awkward denominators such as 17 frequently appear in the solutions. A way to avoid these fractions is to make the equations homogeneous and to use the cross-product procedure. The solution, of course, will also be in the homogeneous form (x_1, x_2, x_3), but this can quickly be converted to the (x, y) form by dividing through by the x_3 value (provided it isn't zero!) and then omitting the final 1. Thus our first solution, $(14, -32, -17)$, becomes $(-14/17, 32/17, 1)$ or simply $(-14/17, 32/17)$.

Before going further, we had better investigate the case where x_3 happens to come out equal to zero in our cross-product operation. It is not difficult to form an example. All we need to do is to make two lines for which the first and second members of the number triple for one line are proportional to the corresponding members of the other triple. Let $e = [3, 2, 5]$ and $f = [6, 4, -7]$ be our lines. Then from

$$
\begin{array}{ccccc}
3 & 2 & 5 & 3 & 2 \\
6 & 4 & -7 & 6 & 4
\end{array}
$$

we find the point of intersection to be $(-34, 51, 0)$, for which an equivalent representation is $(-2, 3, 0)$. Since we cannot divide by zero, the point $(-2, 3, 0)$ apparently has no image in the Cartesian plane. The Cartesian equations for the lines e and f, which are $3x + 2y + 5 = 0$ and $6x + 4y - 7 = 0$, immediately clarify the situation for the student of ordinary analytic geometry. These are the equations of parallel lines which do not intersect in the ordinary Cartesian plane. If we try to solve the equations algebraically by multiplying the members of the first equation by -2 before adding to the second equation, we have an absurdity.

Thus:

$$-6x - 4y - 10 = 0$$
$$6x + 4y - 7 = 0$$
$$\overline{-17 = 0.}$$

Algebraically this is described by saying that the equations are *inconsistent*, i.e. that they have no simultaneous solution. In the extended Cartesian plane the two parallel lines e and f have an ideal point in common. Thus while $(-2, 3, 0)$ has no image in the ordinary Cartesian plane, it does correspond to an ideal point in the extended Cartesian plane.

For postulate P1, we start with two distinct points $A = (a_1, a_2, a_3)$ and $B = (b_1, b_2, b_3)$. The equations of these points are

$$a_1 u_1 + a_2 u_2 + a_3 u_3 = 0$$
$$b_1 u_1 + b_2 u_2 + b_3 u_3 = 0,$$

and we now seek a line $c = [c_1, c_2, c_3]$ satisfying the incidence conditions

$$a_1 c_1 + a_2 c_2 + a_3 c_3 = 0$$
$$b_1 c_1 + b_2 c_2 + b_3 c_3 = 0.$$

Since these equations are identical with (II.2), the solutions for the c's will be identical with (II.3).

Again, perhaps we need an illustration. Let A be $(4, 3, 7)$ and B be $(-2, 1, 5)$. Forming the cross product from

$$
\begin{array}{ccccc}
4 & 3 & 7 & 4 & 3 \\
-2 & 1 & 5 & -2 & 1,
\end{array}
$$

we find our line AB to be $[8, -34, 10]$ or $[4, -17, 5]$; i.e. the equation of the line is $4x_1 - 17x_2 + 5x_3 = 0$.

Once again it is interesting to consider the corresponding situation in the Cartesian plane. The image points there are $(\frac{4}{7}, \frac{3}{7})$

and $(-\frac{2}{5}, \frac{1}{5})$, and the equation of the line passing through these points is $4x - 17y + 5 = 0$ (found rather laboriously in ordinary analytic geometry from the "two-point equation" or by first finding the slope and then using the "point-slope equation.")

Since there have been some digressions, it may be well to summarize the results of this section. First, we gave an algebraic formulation for the real projective plane, where a triple of real numbers such as a_1, a_2, a_3, other than the zero triple, represents *either* a point (a_1, a_2, a_3) *or* a line $[a_1, a_2, a_3]$, depending on the marks of enclosure used. The triple ka_1, ka_2, ka_3, with $k \neq 0$, is not to be considered as a triple different from a_1, a_2, a_3 but merely as another way of writing a_1, a_2, a_3. The point (x_1, x_2, x_3) and the line $[u_1, u_2, u_3]$ are incident if and only if the dot product $x \cdot u$ equals zero. Two distinct points $A = (a_1, a_2, a_3)$ and $B = (b_1, b_2, b_3)$ are *always* incident with exactly one line $c = [c_1, c_2, c_3]$, where $c \sim [A \times B]$, and two distinct lines $a = [a_1, a_2, a_3]$ and $b = [b_1, b_2, b_3]$ are *always* incident with exactly one point $C = (c_1, c_2, c_3)$, where $C \sim (a \times b)$. The cross-product operation, for which a simple mnemonic device has been given, thus becomes a very important one. This simple arithmetic calculation enables us to find quickly the intersections of lines and the joins of points and thus prove theorems that depend only on incidence. We remind the reader of the statement of Hilbert, "The theorems relating to incidence are by far the most important theorems of projective geometry."

Our definitions of point, line, and incidence are completely analytic; that is, in themselves they have nothing to do with geometric pictures. However we can always go to a Cartesian model—frequently we shall prefer a model in the extended Cartesian plane—if we want a Cartesian interpretation of a projective theorem. Once again, however, we emphasize that the concepts of distance, angle, parallelism, perpendicularity, which we find difficult to ignore in the Cartesian plane, are not introduced in projective geometry. Finally, our analytic formulation of the real projective plane is such that we are able to see how this field of mathematics can be generalized, and how it inevitably becomes more abstract as it is generalized. It is hoped that the following quotations will now mean more to the reader than they would have meant if he had not previously read this section. The first quotation is from a book on differential geometry and the second is from a book on topology.

> *Geometry as conceived today, is fundamentally the study of spatial structure. But space in the modern sense is only weakly related to the space of ordinary experience. It is an abstract set of unspecified things which may be referred to a system of labels which possess a certain mathematical structure.*[†]

> *The object whose intrinsic qualitative properties are to be studied can be virtually anything: a geometric figure, a rubber band, a doughnut, a collection of functions, an "abstract space." A property common to all objects of topological study is that they are sets. The elements of the sets will be referred to as* points, *although, as the above examples indicate, the geometric notion of a point is not the only applicable one. A point may be a function, a book, a dog on Main Street, a point in the sense of Euclidean geometry, or just about anything else.*[‡]

II.2   *Euclidean Models of the Real Projective Plane*

We begin this section with a description of a kind of a model for the real projective plane that has certain advantages over the model in the extended Euclidean plane—one where we are not

---

† Gerretsen *27*, p. VII.

‡ Mansfield *47*, p. 2.

tempted to introduce the non-projective properties of distance, parallelism, etc.

For any point of three-dimensional Euclidean space—say the origin O—we consider the totality of lines and the totality of planes passing through this point. We then rename the lines and planes, calling the Euclidean lines through O the points of the projective plane, and the Euclidean planes through O the lines of the projective plane. The incidence relation of a Euclidean line through O lying on a Euclidean plane through O then takes the place of the incidence relation of point lying on a line in the projective plane.

It is now a simple matter to see that the postulates for the most general projective plane are statisfied for these new "points" and "lines." We know that in three-dimensional Euclidean space exactly one plane through O is incident with every two distinct lines through O. Under our renaming, this statement becomes postulate P1, for the projective plane: *Exactly one line is incident with every two distinct points.* Likewise, the Euclidean proposition that exactly one line through O is incident with every two distinct planes through O, becomes postulate P2 for the projective plane: *Exactly one point is incident with every two distinct lines.*

In this new model, there is no suggestion of any *extra*ordinary or *ideal* points or line that we found it necessary to add to the Euclidean plane in order to form the extended Euclidean plane model for the projective plane. The price that we have had to pay is that our projective "points" and "lines" no longer resemble the dots and tracings of a straight edge that we have been accustomed to call points and lines.

The reader who is familiar with the analytic geometry of lines and planes in space will doubtless be pleased to note the equivalence of that analytic geometry with our analytic geometry of the projective plane. For example, the *direction numbers* of two distinct lines through the origin are usually represented by a_1, b_1, c_1 and a_2, b_2, c_2. The equation of the unique plane through the origin which contains these two lines is $Ax + By + Cz = 0$, where A, B, C are the direction numbers of the *normal* to this plane. A, B, C must satisfy the following orthogonality conditions with the direction numbers of the lines:

$$Aa_1 + Bb_1 + Cc_1 = 0$$
$$Aa_2 + Bb_2 + Cc_2 = 0.$$

Thus to determine the plane that is incident with two lines through the origin, two homogeneous linear equations in the three unknowns A, B, C must be solved. This is precisely the algebraic problem (with slightly different notation) that we encountered in the preceding section when we were finding the point that was incident with two distinct lines in the real projective plane. The student of three-dimensional analytic geometry will recognize that the restrictions on sets of direction numbers, namely that the zero triple is excluded and that we are interested merely in three numbers that are proportional to the three direction cosines, are exactly the same conditions that are placed on triples of real numbers used to represent points in the real projective plane. A similar discussion can be given to show that the analytic determination of the direction numbers for the line of intersection of two Euclidean planes through O is equivalent to the determination of the point of intersection of two distinct lines in the projective plane.

A different model for the projective plane may be obtained if we consider a sphere with center at the origin and take as our lines of the projective plane the great circle intersections of the sphere with Euclidean planes through O. For the points of the projective plane we can use the points of intersections of the

Euclidean lines through O with the sphere, provided we agree that two antipodal points of the sphere are to represent the *same* point of the projective plane. This is sometimes called *identifying* diametrically opposed points of the sphere.[16]

II.3   *Plane Duality and Plane Configurations*

We are now ready to discuss one of the most important concepts of plane projective geometry—the *duality principle*. Both in the postulates that we have stated for the most general kind of plane and in the analytic definition of point, line, and incidence, there is a symmetry of point and line.

If in postulate P1—where, we remind the reader, point, line, and incidence are primitive or undefined concepts—we interchange the words point and line, we obtain postulate P2. Likewise, if we make the same interchange in P2, we obtain P1.

In the analytic definitions of point and line, we are talking merely about ordered triples of real numbers (other than the zero triple). A particular triple such as 3, -1, 5 can represent either a point $A = (3, -1, 5)$ or a line $b = [3, -1, 5]$. A point and a line are incident if and only if they satisfy the incidence condition. Since $(3)(3) + (-1)(-1) + (5)(5) = 9 + 1 + 25 = 35 \neq 0$, evidently point A and line b are not incident. On the other hand point $C = (2, 4, -3)$ and line $d = [3, 0, 2]$ are incident since $(2)(3) + (4)(0) + (-3)(2) = 6 + 0 - 6 = 0$. Because the incidence condition

$$x \cdot u = x_1 u_1 + x_2 u_2 + x_3 u_3 = 0$$

is symmetric in the x's and the u's, it is at once evident that line $e = [2, 4, -3]$ and point $F = (3, 0, 2)$ are also incident.

In the preceding section our first illustrative example involved starting with two lines [2, 3, −4] and [5, −1, 6] and finding—by means of the cross-product procedure—the unique point incident with these two lines. This point was found to be (14, −32, −17). When we illustrated the procedure for finding the unique line incident with two distinct points, in order to avoid any possible confusion, we selected two new triples of numbers for the points. Since the two procedures are actually the same algebraically, we now observe that we did more work than was necessary for the second illustration. Having worked out the first illustrative exercise, we could automatically have said that the two points (2, 3, −4) and (5, −1, 6) were incident with the line [14, −32, −17].

Thus interchanging the concepts of point and line in any valid statement or theorem involving only incidence in plane projective geometry immediately gives in turn a valid statement or theorem—the so-called *dual* statement or theorem. The duality principle is a built-in part of our algebraic framework, and the separate proof of a dual theorem (although easily accomplished) is unnecessary. The dual theorem will, in general, have a geometric content that is different from that of the original theorem, but there are important cases where the two are related.

The dual of a statement can, in fact, be the original statement itself. In this case the statement is said to be *self-dual*. We shall shortly have some examples of self-dual statements and figures. The figure that illustrates the very important theorem of Pappus is one of these, and thus by dualizing the theorem of Pappus we are led to another theorem that appears from its statement to be quite different, but which is illustrated by the figure used for the original theorem. Another interesting case is when the dual theorem turns out to be the converse of the original theorem. This happens in the celebrated theorem of Desargues to which Section III.2 will be devoted.

The theorems of Pascal and Brianchon, which are dual theorems, will also be discussed in Chapter III. It is interesting to note here, however, that Blaise Pascal (1623–62) discovered the theorem bearing his name in 1639 (when he was only sixteen years old), but that the dual theorem was unknown until C. J. Brianchon (1785–1864) proved it in 1806. It is frequently difficult to award the proper credit for new discoveries, and this is the case with the principle of duality. However, J. D. Gergonne (1771–1859) was apparently the first—in 1826—to state the principle in definite form.†

For simple illustrations of plane dual figures, we turn now to a generalization of the polygons of elementary geometry. This will give an introduction to the subject of plane configurations which have been called "a particularly instructive part of projective geometry," and about which it has been said that "there was a time when the study of configurations was considered the most important branch of all geometry."‡

A generalized triangle might be defined as a figure consisting of three distinct non-collinear points and three distinct non-concurrent lines, each point being incident with two lines and each line being incident with two points. In other words, a generalized triangle is simply an ordinary triangle with sides prolonged or extended indefinitely. We note that a generalized triangle is a self-dual figure, that only one triangle can be formed from any three given non-collinear points or three non-concurrent lines, and that every pair of points (or lines) of the figure is incident with a line (or point) of the figure.

It would now be natural to define a generalized quadrangle as a self-dual figure consisting of four points, no three of which

---

† See Eves *22*, p. 313.
‡ Hilbert and Cohn-Vossen *36*, p. 95.

are collinear, and four lines, no three of which are concurrent, with each point incident with two lines and each line incident with two points. Let us examine this proposed definition more closely.

We begin by selecting the four points and labeling them *A*, *B*, *C*, *D*. Next we join these points in the alphabetical order, and extend the lines to obtain Figure 25. This figure resembles

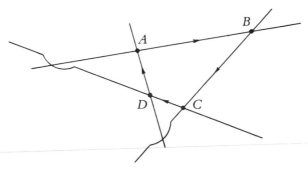

FIGURE 25

the usual picture of a quadrangle *ABCD*. We have tried to indicate in this figure that lines *AB* and *CD* do not meet in a point belonging to our particular quadrangle but do have in common a so-called *cross-over* point. Likewise for lines *AD* and *BC*. The arrows are not a part of the figure but are intended to remind us of the order used in joining the points.

Starting again with our same four points *A*, *B*, *C*, *D*, we now join them in a different order *ABDC* (Figure 26). This figure is quite unlike any quadrangle of elementary geometry, but it certainly satisfies our definition.

A third figure is obtained by joining the points in the order *ACBD* (Figure 27).

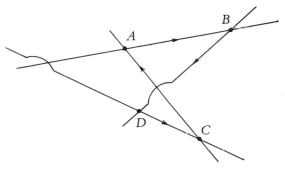

Evidently we could reverse the order of joining the points in each of the three cases (i.e. reverse the direction of the arrows) without obtaining different pictures, and evidently also in each case we could start with any one of the four points. A little experimentation will convince the reader that we have constructed all of the essentially different quadrangles that can be constructed

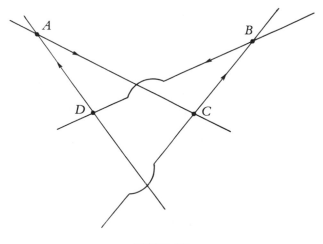

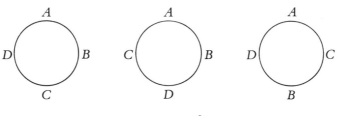

FIGURE 28

by joining our four points in different orders. That is, there are only three different *cyclic* orders of the four letters *A*, *B*, *C*, *D*. These can be illustrated in the diagram of Figure 28.

In addition to obtaining three different generalized quadrangles from a given set of four points, we note that in each of Figures 25, 26, 27 there are two pairs of points that are not joined by any lines of the figure. This would suggest drawing a single figure—which might be thought of as a composite of the three that we

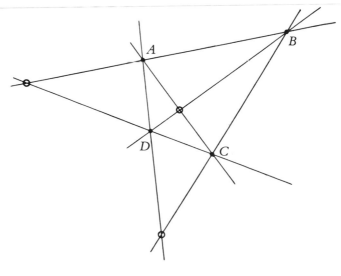

FIGURE 29

have drawn—in which every pair of points is incident with a line
of the figure (Figure 29). This latest figure consists of four points
and six lines, each point incident with three lines and each line
incident with two points. The cross-over points—shown in
Figure 29 with small circles around them—are not a part of the
configuration, but they can be used to define what is called a
diagonal triangle associated with the configuration. (We have not
drawn the "sides" of this triangle.)

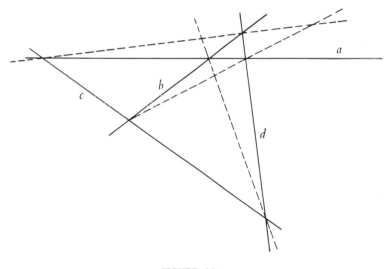

FIGURE 30

Figure 29 is evidently not self-dual, but its dual—consisting
of six points and four lines, each point incident with two lines
and each line incident with three points—is easily constructed
(Figure 30). Instead of starting with four points, we now start
with four lines (no three if which are concurrent), and instead
of constructing the six joins of pairs of points, we now locate
the six intersections of pairs of lines. The dotted lines in Figure 30

are not a part of this configuration but can be used to define the diagonal triangle associated with it.

We now see that we have two kinds of generalized figures that can be constructed from four (or more) points or lines. The adjective *simple* is frequently used for the first kind (Figures 25, 26, 27), and *complete*, for the second kind (Figures 29, 30). To distinguish between the configurations of Figure 29 and Figure 30, we shall use the expression *complete 4-point* for Figure 29, where we started with four points, and *complete 4-line* for Figure 30, where we started with four lines. Complete 5-points, 5-lines, etc. can evidently be defined and constructed, but we shall have no need for these.

Returning to the self-dual configurations in Figures 25, 26, 27, instead of calling them simple 4-points or simple 4-lines (as is sometimes done), we shall merely call them (generalized) quadrangles. Although literally the word quadrangle means four angles—and we are not interested in angles—at least it is neutral as far as points and lines are concerned. (Thus we shall not use the word quadrilateral because of its partiality to lines.) For simple 5-points or 5-lines, 6-points, etc., we shift from Latin to Greek and use pentagon, hexagon, etc., (where *gon* comes from γωνια meaning angle). Our definition then, for what we shall call a generalized polygon in the plane is the following:

A generalized polygon in the plane is a set of n points (lines) of the plane taken in a definite order, in which no three consecutive points (lines) are collinear (concurrent), together with the n lines (points) incident with successive points (lines).

Following ordinary usage, we shall refer to the points as *vertices* and the lines as *sides* of the polygons, and shall omit the adjective *generalized* unless there is danger of ambiguity.

The reader may well wonder why we have devoted so much space to what appears to be an almost trivial subject. He will soon discover that some of these queer-looking polygons will be very useful in describing certain situations that would otherwise require a great many words to clarify. For example, we shall shortly be concerned with Figure 31. A simple description of this figure (paying no attention to the little circles around three of the points) is to say that it consists of a generalized hexagon *ABCDEF* whose

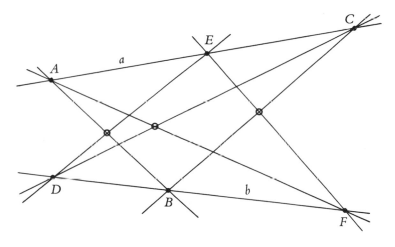

FIGURE 31

six vertices lie alternately on two lines *a* and *b*. The reader should trace the hexagon, say by starting at *A*, then going to *B*, to *C*, etc., and finally returning from *F* to *A*.

In our consideration of the above hexagon, we shall need to identify the pairs of what we shall call opposite sides, following the usage in an ordinary hexagon. This is awkward in our figure, but we can introduce some very helpful notation for this purpose.

We first draw an ordinary hexagon (Figure 32) with vertices labeled in the same order as in Figure 31. Here, the pairs of opposite sides are clearly *AB* and *DE*, *BC* and *EF*, *CD* and *FA*, where

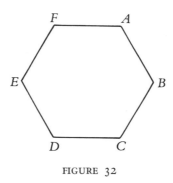

pairs are obtained by selecting two consecutive vertices, then skipping the next one and taking the following pair. By writing the six letters in a row and repeating the first one, we can introduce symbols as follows to identify the pairs of opposite sides:

$$A \quad B \quad C \quad D \quad E \quad F \quad A$$

The reader can now make a simple discovery that would have made his name well known in mathematics if he had been the first person to make (and prove) the discovery. He should locate the *intersections* of the pairs of opposite sides of the hexagon of Figure 31. These are indicated by the points with small circles around them. They look as if they might be collinear, but of course this may be simply an accident in our figure, i.e. caused by the location of lines *a* and *b* and choice of points *A*, *B*, *C*, etc. Before trying to prove that these intersection points are always collinear, he will want to draw some different pictures. (The reader should be warned that he is now skirting the edge of a dangerous precipice. No matter how many carefully drawn pictures he

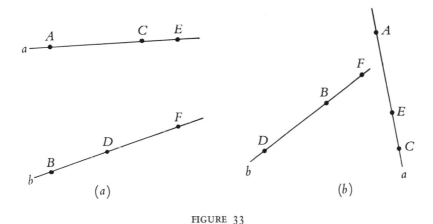

FIGURE 33

makes, these will not constitute a proof.[17] They could, however, be considered as supporting evidence for the conjecture that these points will always be collinear. The theorem still remains to be proved.) The approximate locations of given lines and points in Figure 33(a and b) are suggested to give some figures that will appear to be quite different from Figure 31. The reader should trace these on a sheet of paper and then complete the construction as in Figure 31.

If the reader still feels that he is being asked to consider something that is essentially trivial, we close this digression with an additional quotation from the writings of the distinguished mathematician quoted earlier which states that the theorem indicated above "is the only significant theorem on incidence in the plane," and that the configuration which illustrates this theorem "thus represents the most important figure in plane geometry."[†]

The proof of this theorem together with some indication of its importance will be given in the next section. In the following

---

† Hilbert and Cohn-Vossen *36*, p. 132.

section it will be shown that the important theorem of Desargues is a consequence of this theorem (which is known as the theorem of Pappus).

In the preceding paragraphs we have used the term *configuration* informally as if it were a synonym for *figure*. It is now high time that we give a formal definition. A *plane configuration* is defined to be a system of p points and L straight lines arranged in a plane in such a way that every point of the system is incident with a fixed number λ of straight lines of the system, and every straight line of the system is incident with a fixed number π of points of the system.[18] A convenient symbol to characterize such a system is $(p_\lambda \, L_\pi)$. The complete 4-point satisfies the definition of a configuration and is denoted by $(4_3 6_2)$. The dual configuration—the complete 4-line—is denoted by $(6_2 4_3)$.

The first question that will doubtless occur to the reader is whether or not all of the integers p, L, λ, π can be chosen arbitrarily for a configuration. For the complete 4-point, with three lines passing through each of the four points, it would appear that we should have twelve lines. However, each line is to pass through two points, therefore in obtaining this number of lines we have counted each line twice and the correct number is $(4 \cdot 3)/2 = 6$. Generalizing this argument, we see that $(p \cdot \lambda)/\pi = L$, i.e. the following relation must be satisfied for a configuration:

$$p \cdot \lambda = L \cdot \pi.$$

Particularly interesting configurations are those for which the number of points is equal to the number of lines. With $p = L$, we must evidently have $\pi = \lambda$. The configuration symbol thus becomes $(p_\lambda \, p_\lambda)$, for which the more concise notation p_λ is used. Such configurations are evidently self-dual. We now begin a systematic investigation of these configurations p_λ for $\lambda = 1, 2, 3, \dots$.[19]

For $\lambda = 1$, the configuration p_1 would consist of a system of p points, each incident with only one line of the system. For $p = 1$, we have the trivial situation of one point with one line passing through it. For $p = 2$, our system would consist of two points each with a line passing through it. The same line could not be incident with both points, and the two lines could not have a point of the configuration in common, since each line of the configuration is to be incident with only one point of the configuration. Thus for $p = 2$ and for $p > 2$, the p_1 configurations would consist of separated parts. Although previously we did not specify that the configurations should be all in one piece, i.e. be connected and not decomposable into separate figures, this now appears to be an additional qualification that is desirable. Thus for $\lambda = 1$, 1_1 is the only (non-decomposable) configuration. Likewise, for $\lambda = 2$, the configurations p_2 are not very exciting. Here they consist merely of the generalized polygons that we discussed earlier.

For $\lambda = 3$, the situation becomes more interesting. At once we can see that there must be at least seven points (and seven straight lines) in the configuration. Through any point, there pass three lines, and on each of these there are two additional points. Thus two times three plus our original point gives seven as the minimum value for p (Figure 34).

The cases of $p = 9$, 10 are the important ones for us, but before discussing these, we shall say a few words about $p = 7$, 8.[†]

Instead of our usual notation for points and lines, it will be convenient at this time to denote both points and lines by integers. We shall enclose integers representing lines in brackets but shall

---

[†] If the reader wants further details, he will find them in Hilbert and Cohn-Vossen *36*, Chap. III, in Levi *45*, in Coxeter *17*, or in Argunov and Skornyakov *3*.

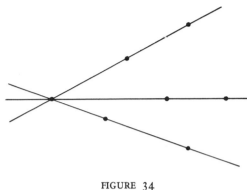

merely use integers without marks of enclosure to represent points.

In discussing a particular configuration such as the 7_3, it is very helpful to have what is called a configuration table. It can be shown that there is essentially only one such table for the 7_3[†] (Figure 35).

	The 7 lines						
	[1]	[2]	[3]	[4]	[5]	[6]	[7]
The 3 points	1	1	1	2	2	3	3
on each	2	4	6	4	5	4	5
line	3	5	7	6	7	7	6

FIGURE 35

It is not difficult to see that three conditions must have been satisfied in forming this table. First, there must be no duplication of integers in any column since there must be three distinct

---

[†] For details, see Hilbert and Cohn-Vossen *36*.

points on each line. Second, two different columns cannot have a pair of integers in common without having the corresponding lines coincide. And finally, every integer must occur exactly three times since every point is to be incident with three straight lines.

The existence of a configuration table, it should be pointed out, does not insure that the configuration can be "realized," i.e. be constructed, in the Euclidean plane. In other words, the three conditions of the preceding paragraph are necessary but not sufficient for the existence of a geometrical figure corresponding to the table. Later we shall investigate the realization of the 7_3

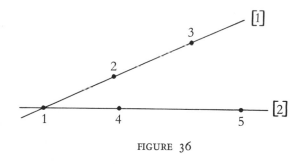

FIGURE 36

in the real projective plane (and by inference in the Euclidean plane), but for the present we merely attempt to make the constructions that are suggested by the table and see what happens. We first construct lines [1] and [2] (Figure 36). Considering next lines [4] and [7], we see that the intersection of lines through points 2, 4 and 3, 5 determine point 6. In like manner, a consideration of lines [5] and [6] shows that the lines through points 2, 5 and 3, 4 determine point 7 (Figure 37). From the table, line [3] is to contain points 1, 6, 7. This certainly is not the case in our figure, and as soon as we notice that points 1, 6, 7 are the vertices of the diagonal triangle for the complete 4-point formed from

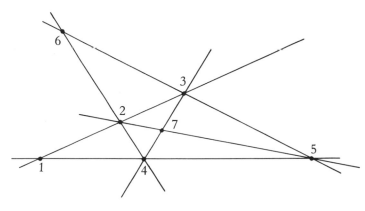

FIGURE 37

the points 2, 3, 4, 5, we probably suspect that points 1, 6, 7 can *never* be collinear in ordinary plane geometry. This would appear to make the 7_3 configuration devoid of all interest. Actually, however the 7_3 is a very important configuration in parts of projective geometry. In Chapter IV we shall give a schematic figure for the 7_3.

For the 8_3, it can be shown that there is again essentially only one possible table (Figure 38). Likewise, it can be shown that the

[1]	[2]	[3]	[4]	[5]	[6]	[7]	[8]
1	1	1	2	2	3	3	5
2	4	6	4	5	4	6	7
3	5	7	8	6	7	8	8

FIGURE 38

8_3 cannot be realized in the real projective plane. It can be realized in the complex projective plane, and a procedure for investigating this will be indicated in Chapter IV.

When we come to the case of $p = 9$, the situation changes. Here it can be shown that there are three different tables, and that all three configurations can be realized in the real plane. The customary notation is to use $(9_3)_1$, $(9_3)_2$, and $(9_3)_3$ as the symbols for the three configurations of type 9_3. One of these is much more important than the others, and naturally it is the one denoted by $(9_3)_1$. Instead of starting with this one, for reasons that will soon be apparent, we first consider one of the others. Tables for $(9_3)_2$ and $(9_3)_3$ are given in Figures 39 and 40.

The $(9_3)_2$

[1]	[2]	[3]	[4]	[5]	[6]	[7]	[8]	[9]
1	1	1	2	2	3	3	4	5
2	4	6	4	7	5	7	8	6
3	5	7	6	8	8	9	9	9

FIGURE 39

The $(9_3)_3$

[1]	[2]	[3]	[4]	[5]	[6]	[7]	[8]	[9]
1	1	1	2	2	3	3	4	7
2	4	6	5	6	4	5	6	8
3	5	7	8	9	9	7	8	9

FIGURE 40

If the reader tries to construct $(9_3)_2$ step by step, it is highly probable that he will find, as in Figure 41, that the three points for the last line to be constructed are not collinear.

We say "highly probable" because there is an outside chance that this will not happen—as in Figure 42. Thus, for the $(9_3)_2$, the configuration can be constructed in the real plane but special

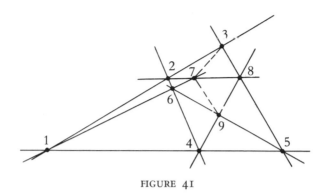

FIGURE 41

care must be taken in the matter of the choice of starting lines and points. A similar situation holds for the $(9_3)_3$.

We now give the table for the $(9_3)_1$ (Figure 43) and attempt to see how this configuration differs from the $(9_3)_2$ and the $(9_3)_3$.

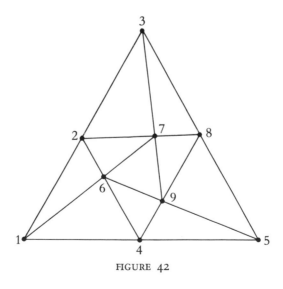

FIGURE 42

The $(9_3)_1$

[1]	[2]	[3]	[4]	[5]	[6]	[7]	[8]	[9]
1	1	1	2	2	3	3	4	5
2	4	6	4	7	5	6	6	7
3	5	7	8	9	9	8	9	8

FIGURE 43

Many readers have probably guessed what lies ahead. If the $(9_3)_1$ is such an important configuration in projective geometry, the last line to be constructed should *automatically* contain the three points given by the table. In other words, for the $(9_3)_1$, as contrasted with the $(9_3)_2$, *no* special care need be taken with the choice of starting lines and points. This reminds us of Figure 31 (with the addition of the line through the three circled points) and the completed Figures 33a and b. Since each of these figures consists of nine points and nine lines, each point incident with three lines and each line incident with three points, it is a good guess that they will be pictorial representations for the table for the $(9_3)_1$. The integers 1, ... , 9 which were used to represent points in the table for the $(9_3)_1$ can replace the letters in Figure 31 in various ways and still have the configuration incidences of the table satisfied, e.g. have points 1, 2, 3 collinear as required by the first column of the table. One of these replacements is shown in Figure 44.

Of course, we still haven't proved that the last three constructed points (5, 7, 8 in Fig. 44) are always collinear. As indicated earlier, the theorem which states this fact is known as the theroem of Pappus, and it will be proved in the first section of the next chapter.

For $p = 10$, there are ten different configurations 10_3, all but one of which can be realized in the real plane. Again, one of

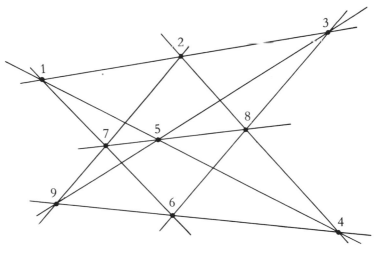

FIGURE 44

these—the configuration of Desargues—is much more important than the others. The corresponding theorem of Desargues will be proved in Section III.2, and it will also be shown that the theorem of Desargues in the plane is a consequence of the theorem of Pappus.

We conclude this section by giving the table of incidences for the configuration of Desargues, i.e. the $(10_3)_1$ (Figure 45).

[1]	[2]	[3]	[4]	[5]	[6]	[7]	[8]	[9]	[10]
1	1	1	2	2	3	3	4	5	8
2	4	6	4	6	5	7	6	7	9
3	5	7	8	9	8	9	10	10	10

FIGURE 45

III

Some Theorems
of
Plane Projective Geometry

III.I   *The Theorem of Pappus*[†]

The theorem of Pappus may be stated as follows:

If the six (distinct) vertices of a hexagon lie alternately on two straight lines,[‡] then the three points of intersection of pairs of opposite sides are collinear.

In Figure 46, if the given lines are taken as l_1 and l_2, then the hexagon is $A_1 B_2 C_1 A_2 B_1 C_2$, and the pairs of opposite sides (and their intersections) are given by the following scheme:

$$A_1 \; B_2 \; C_1 \; A_2 \; B_1 \; C_2 \; A_1$$

$$\underline{\hspace{3em}} \quad \underline{\hspace{2em}} \qquad C_3$$
$$\underline{\hspace{3em}} \quad \underline{\hspace{2em}} \qquad A_3$$
$$\underline{\hspace{3em}} \quad \underline{\hspace{2em}} \qquad B_3$$

[†] For a reason that will be apparent later, this theorem is sometimes referred to as the Pappus-Pascal theorem (see Argunov and Skornyakov *3*, p. 9).

[‡] With no vertex of the hexagon at the intersection of the two lines for the general case.

The theorem now states that these points of intersection, A_3, B_3, C_3, are *always* collinear (on a line that is sometimes called the Pappus line of the figure).

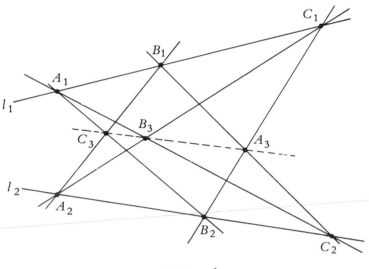

FIGURE 46

Before starting the proof of this theorem, we remind the reader of the so-called "analytic proofs" of theorems concerning triangles, etc., that are given in all textbooks on analytic geometry. The simplicity of these proofs arises from a proper location of the figure relative to the coordinate axes. If one wishes to prove a theorem about *any* triangle, he may take one vertex at the origin, another vertex on say the x-axis, and the third at some general point not on either axis as in Figure 47(a). Or, as in Figure 47(b), he may take two vertices on one axis and the third on the other axis. The zeros that appear in the coordinates materially reduce the labor in later computations.

Similar simplifications are available for analytic proofs in the real projective plane. For example, it can be shown that any four points of the plane, no three of which are collinear, may be taken as $(1, 0, 0)$, $(0, 1, 0)$, $(0, 0, 1)$ and $(1, 1, 1)$. Hence with no loss of

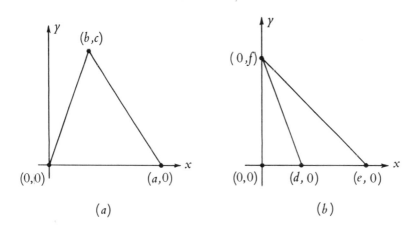

FIGURE 47

generality, we designate four of the points of Figure 46 to be the following: $A_1 = (1, 0, 0)$, $A_2 = (0, 1, 0)$, $A_3 = (0, 0, 1)$ and $C_1 = (1, 1, 1)$. We then find the equations of the lines A_1C_1, A_2C_1, and A_3C_1. For A_1C_1, using our cross-product procedure, we have

$$
\begin{array}{ccccc}
1 & 0 & 0 & 1 & 0 \\
1 & 1 & 1 & 1 & 1,
\end{array}
$$

and $A_1C_1 = [0, -1, 1] \sim [0, 1, -1]$. Hence the equation of A_1C_1 is $x_2 - x_3 = 0$. In similar fashion we find the equations of A_2C_1 and A_3C_1 to be $x_1 - x_3 = 0$ and $x_1 - x_2 = 0$. We now choose three arbitrary points B_1, B_3, and B_2 on the lines A_1C_1, A_2C_1, and A_3C_1. B_1 could evidently be represented by (b_1, b_2, b_2) with

$b_1 \neq b_2$ and $b_2 \neq 0$ (so that B_1 is distinct from C_1 and A_1 for the general case. Special cases will be considered later). A simpler representation, however, is given by $(d, 1, 1)$ with $d \neq 1$. Likewise B_3 can be taken as $(1, e, 1)$ with $e \neq 1$, and B_2 as $(1, 1, f)$ with $f \neq 1$.

Our method will now be to determine C_3 and C_2 by incidence requirements and to show that the same condition on d, e, f is necessary to give each of these sets of incidences, i.e. when the condition on d, e, f is satisfied to require lines A_1B_2, A_2B_1, and A_3B_3 to meet in C_3, then *automatically* lines A_1B_3, A_3B_1, and A_2B_2 will meet in C_2, or vice versa.

To find the equation of A_1B_2 we have

$$
\begin{array}{ccccc}
1 & 0 & 0 & 1 & 0 \\
1 & 1 & f & 1 & 1,
\end{array}
$$

whence $A_1B_2 = [0, -f, 1] \sim [0, f, -1]$. Thus the equation of A_1B_2 is $fx_2 - x_3 = 0$. Similarly, the equations of A_2B_1 and A_3B_3 are found to be $dx_3 - x_1 = 0$ and $ex_1 - x_2 = 0$. The intersection of A_1B_2 and A_2B_1 is found from

$$
\begin{array}{ccccc}
0 & f & -1 & 0 & f \\
-1 & 0 & d & -1 & 0
\end{array}
$$

to be $(d \cdot f, 1, f)$ and this point will lie on A_3B_3 if and only if $e \cdot d \cdot f - 1 = 0$ or $e \cdot d \cdot f = 1$.

In like manner, equations of A_1B_3, A_3B_1, and A_2B_2 are found to be $x_2 - ex_3 = 0$, $x_1 - dx_2 = 0$ and $x_3 - fx_1 = 0$. The point of intersection of A_1B_3 and A_3B_1 is found to be $(de, e, 1)$ and this point will lie on A_2B_2 if and only if $1 - fde = 0$ or $fde = 1$. Since multiplication is commutative for real numbers, this condition is equivalent to the one found in the preceding paragraph. Hence, we have proved the theorem of Pappus for the general case where the vertices of the hexagon are distinct. The resulting figure is the Pappus configuration $(9_3)_1$, and another way of phrasing the Pappus theorem is to say that if we have constructed eight of the nine incidences from the $(9_3)_1$ configuration table, then the ninth one must always follow. Remember that this was not true for the $(9_3)_2$ and the $(9_3)_3$.

Using the notation of Figure 46, the incidence table corresponding to the Pappus configuration may be written in the form of Figure 48. In this notation, the three points A_i, B_j, C_h are collinear whenever $i + j + h$ is a multiple of 3.

l_1	l_2	l_3	l_4	l_5	l_6	l_7	l_8	l_9
A_1	A_2	A_3	A_1	A_2	A_3	A_1	A_2	A_3
B_1	B_2	B_3	B_2	B_3	B_1	B_3	B_1	B_2
C_1	C_2	C_3	C_3	C_1	C_2	C_2	C_3	C_1

FIGURE 48

Let us now consider the *converse* of the theorem of Pappus. If the three points of intersection of pairs of opposite sides of a hexagon are collinear, does it follow that the six vertices of the hexagon must lie alternately on two lines? A little experimentation in the construction of a figure will quickly convince the reader that the converse is *not* true. This immediately raises the following question. If, under the hypothesis that the three points of intersection of pairs of opposite sides of a hexagon are collinear it does *not* follow that the six vertices of the hexagon lie on two lines, can *anything* be said about the location of the six vertices? We have not progressed far enough in our development of real projective geometry in the plane to be able to answer this question. However, if we consider the corresponding situation in a Cartesian (or affine) model, we can anticipate the answer to be given later.

In ordinary analytic geometry we know that the equations of circles, ellipses, parabolas and hyperbolas are all of second degree in x and y, and that conversely all second-degree equations in x and y that have real graphs, represent either these curves or what are called degenerate cases. For example, the equation $x^2 - y^2 = 0$ makes us think of the equation of the hyperbola $x^2 - y^2 = 1$. However, $x^2 - y^2$ factors into $x - y$ times $x + y$. Pairs of coordinates that satisfy either $x - y = 0$ or $x + y = 0$ evidently satisfy $x^2 - y^2 = 0$. Therefore, the graph of $x^2 - y^2 = 0$ consists of the graphs of the two lines represented by the equations $x - y = 0$ and $x + y = 0$, and thus $x^2 - y^2 = 0$ is said to represent a *degenerate* hyperbola, i.e., a hyperbola which has degenerated into two intersecting straight lines. It should now occur to us that the theorem of Pappus, involving two straight lines (a degenerate case of a conic section) in its hypothesis, may be merely a special case of a more general theorem. What would happen, for example, if we started with six vertices of our hexagon inscribed in a circle rather than on two straight lines?

The special case of a *regular* hexagon inscribed in a circle is a good starting place (Figure 49). Since the opposite sides of this hexagon are parallel, the points of intersection of pairs of opposite sides are now the ideal points A_3^*, B_3^*, and C_3^* in the extended Euclidean plane. These points are collinear on the ideal line, and hence our conjectured theorem is true for this case. Our experience with the idea of central projection in space next leads us to suspect that we can project Figure 49 onto another plane in such a way that the hexagon is no longer regular and the line $A_3^* B_3^* C_3^*$ becomes an ordinary line of the plane. Finally, we recall that all non-degenerate conics are projectively equivalent,[†] and we now

---

† See pp. 15–16.

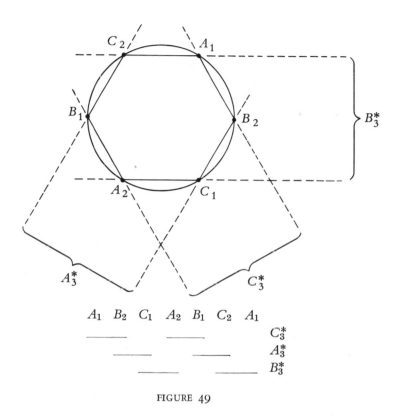

FIGURE 49

feel fairly certain that the following general theorem holds in projective geometry.[20]

If the six vertices of a hexagon lie on a (non-degenerate) conic, then the three points of intersection of pairs of opposite sides are collinear.

The theorem we have just stated is the theorem of Pascal, and its special case (for a degenerate conic consisting of two straight lines) is the theorem of Pappus. So far we have not defined conics in the real analytic projective plane, but later we shall indicate how this can be done, and then we shall devote a section to Pascal's theorem, its applications and extensions, and to the dual theorem discovered by Brianchon.

Some readers, however, may want to experiment geometrically with Pascal's theorem at the present time, and for them we insert a few words of advice. One of the irritating aspects of constructing figures with the ruler alone is that so often key intersections refuse

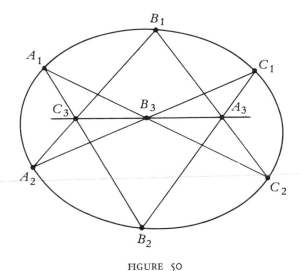

FIGURE 50

to take place on the drawing paper. This difficulty can frequently be avoided by a judicious location of starting points. Consider Figure 50, where the vertices of a hexagon have been placed on an ellipse in such a way that they interlace—so to speak—in a manner reminiscent of the vertices lying alternately on the two lines for the theorem of Pappus. Here we have forced the points A_3, B_3, C_3 to lie where we can reach them.

Incidentally, an additional and useful notation for keeping track of incidences in the Pappus and Pascal theorems is the so-called *cross-join scheme* shown in Figure 51, which is suggested by Figures 46 and 50.

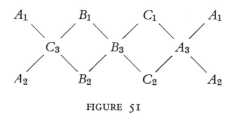

FIGURE 51

Returning to the theorem of Pappus, let us next consider the dual theorem. This means that in our statement on page 81 we simply interchange the concepts of point and line (modifying certain descriptive phrases accordingly since we did not use the incidence terminology). The dual theorem can thus be stated as follows:

If the six sides of a hexagon pass alternately through two points, then the three joins of pairs of opposite vertices are concurrent.[†]

Because of the existence of the principle of plane duality in our geometry, this theorem does not require a proof. Also, since the Pappus configuration is self-dual, we can evidently illustrate our dual theorem with a figure which is basically Figure 46 (Figure 52). On Figure 52, the six vertices of the hexagon are B_1, C_3, B_2, C_2, B_3, C_1, and the sides—joining these points in order —pass alternately through the points A_2 and A_1. Pairs of opposite vertices are B_1 and C_2, B_3 and C_3, B_2 and C_1. Lines passing through these pairs are concurrent at A_3.

[†] This is sometimes called Brianchon's theorem since it is a special case of his more general theorem (see Section III.3).

In our analytic proof of the theorem of Pappus, we obtained the condition for the concurrency of lines A_1B_2, A_2B_1 and A_3B_3 to be $e \cdot d \cdot f - 1$. Then, when we obtained the corresponding condition for the concurrency of lines A_1B_3, A_3B_1, A_2B_2 we wrote the condition as $f \cdot d \cdot e = 1$. This was followed by the comment that these

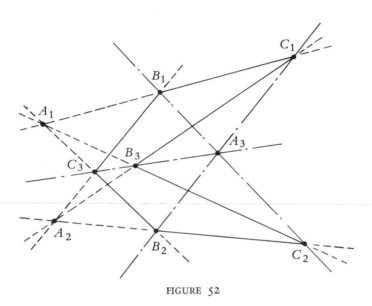

FIGURE 52

two conditions were equivalent since we were dealing with real numbers and multiplication is commutative for real numbers. Many readers were probably mystified by this procedure. They were probably thinking, "*Of course* $e \cdot d \cdot f = f \cdot d \cdot e$ (and both are equal to $d \cdot e \cdot f$). Why bother to comment on this?"

One of the fascinating and important developments in modern mathematics has been the establishment of "the essential structural identity of projective geometry and linear algebra."[†] Hilbert—in

† Baer 5, p. v. See also Rosenbaum 56 and Kuiper 43.

his classical studies on the Foundations of Geometry[21]—placed the cornerstones for much of this development, and one of these concerns the equivalence of the geometric theorem of Pappus with the commutative postulate for multiplication in the underlying number system.[†] Hence we have followed Coxeter[‡] in phrasing the analytic proof of the theorem of Pappus in the real projective plane in such a way that it is apparent that the commutative postulate for multiplication is necessary. If the reader is aware that there are "number" systems in which the commutative postulate for multiplication does not hold, he should then be prepared for the existence of projective planes in which the theorem of Pappus does not hold. We shall defer further discussion of such planes, and of the possible status of the theorem of Pappus as a postulate in synthetic projective geometry until after we have discussed the theorem of Desargues. For the present at least, the reader now probably begins to have some comprehension of the background for the statements by Hilbert quoted on page 71, of the preceding chapter of this book. This will be amplified in the following section when we show that the theorem of Desargues in the plane is a consequence of the the theorem of Pappus.

We shall leave to the reader the investigation of the case of the theorem of Pappus when one of the vertices of the hexagon is the intersection of the given lines, and also the special cases in which certain vertices of the hexagon coincide. First he will probably want to consider by means of the geometric construction what happens to the line $A_3B_3C_3$ when not all of the six vertices of the hexagon are distinct. The following situations (in which vertices not explicitly mentioned are assumed distinct) are suggested:

1. When two vertices on one of the given lines coincide, e.g., $A_1 = B_1$ or $B_2 = C_2$, etc.

---

† See Hilbert *35*.
‡ *17*, p. 432, and *19*, p. 236.

2. When one vertex of one line coincides with a permissible vertex of the other line, e.g., $A_1 = A_2$, or $B_1 = B_2$, or $C_1 = C_2$ (it is evidently *not permissible* for, say, vertex A_1 to coincide with vertex B_2 or C_2 since sides A_1B_2 or A_1C_2 could not then be constructed).
3. A combination of (1) and (2), e.g. $A_1 = A_2$ *and* $B_1 = C_1$.
4. The first case happening on *both* lines, e.g., $A_1 = B_1$ *and* $A_2 = B_2$.

A specialization of the theorem of Pappus not involving coincident vertices is of considerable interest in certain portions of projective geometry. Let us start with the two arbitrary lines l_1 and l_2 which are to contain the (distinct) vertices of our hexagon. However, instead of taking the vertices at random on these lines, let us locate them so that the lines A_1A_2, B_1B_2 and C_1C_2 are concurrent at point D (Figure 53). If the reader now constructs the Pappus line, $l_3 = A_3B_3C_3$, he will find that it appears to pass through the intersection of lines l_1 and l_2. We outline a procedure that will

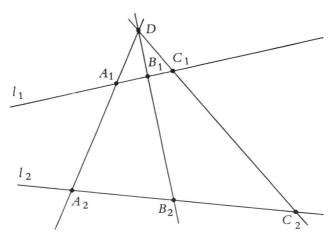

FIGURE 53

enable him to *prove* that this is the case. Starting with points $A_1 = (1, 0, 0)$, $A_2 = (0, 1, 0)$, $B_1 = (d, 1, 1)$, $B_2 = (1, 1, f)$, $C_1 = (1, 1, 1)$, $C_2 = (de, e, 1)$ from our earlier work (and remembering that $d \cdot e \cdot f = 1$), he should find the equations of $A_1 A_2$, $B_1 B_2$, $C_1 C_2$ and then determine the additional condition on d, e, f so that the point of intersection of two of them lies on the third, i.e., so that the three lines are concurrent at D. He will then find that when this condition is incorporated in the equations for l_2 and l_3 as previously found, it will be a simple matter to show that lines l_1, l_2, l_3 are concurrent at a point that we might denote as E.

A "practical" by-product of the preceding paragraph is a straight-edge method for constructing a line through a given point and the inaccessible intersection of two given lines. Consider the plight of a surveyor without boots or a boat who needs to establish a line through a point P and the intersection of the lines l_1 and l_2 in Figure 54. Can you help him to solve his problem?[22]

Before leaving the theorem of Pappus, the reader should become familiar with its affine counterparts, i.e. the forms the theorem takes when constructed in the extended Euclidean, or the

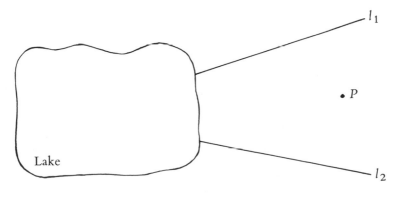

FIGURE 54

affine, plane. If one (and only one) of the hexagon vertices, say C_1, is an ideal point C_1^*, the reader can quickly verify the construction in Figure 55 by using the accompanying scheme. We leave to

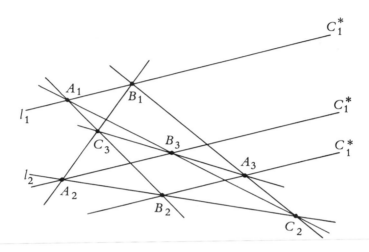

$$A_1 \quad B_2 \quad C_1^* \quad A_2 \quad B_1 \quad C_2 \quad A_1$$

		C_3
———	———	A_3
———	———	B_3

FIGURE 55

the reader the construction when one point on each line is ideal, and also the case when two points on one line are ideal. (In the last case, what must be true of the third point on the line containing the two ideal points, and hence of the line itself?) Additional cases to be investigated (which appear to be different but which are actually covered by the cases above with a relettering of the figure) are when one or all three of the points on the Pappus line are ideal.[23]

III.2   *The Theorem of Desargues*

The neatest way of phrasing the theorem of Desargues appears to be in terms of the concept of perspective triangles. Two plane triangles $A_1B_1C_1$ and $A_2B_2C_2$ are said to be perspective from the point O if lines joining corresponding vertices, i.e. lines A_1A_2, B_1B_2, C_1C_2, all pass through O (the center of perspectivity for the triangles) (Figure 56). The same triangles are said to be perspective

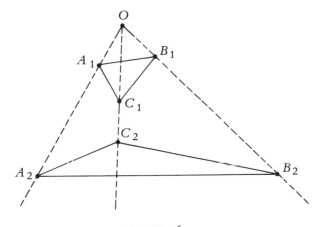

FIGURE 56

from a line (the axis of perspectivity) if corresponding sides meet in three points, P, Q, R, on this line (Figure 57). Since triangles are self-dual figures, the reader can quickly verify that the dual concept of two triangles (3-points) perspective from a point is two triangles (3-lines) perspective from a line.

The theorem of Desargues can now be stated as follows:

If two (distinct) triangles are perspective from a point,[†] they are perspective from a line.

[†] Not on either triangle for the general case.

The plane figure which illustrates this theorem consists of ten points and ten lines, with three lines on each point and three points on each line. It is thus a self-dual configuration, a 10_3, called the *configuration of Desargues*.

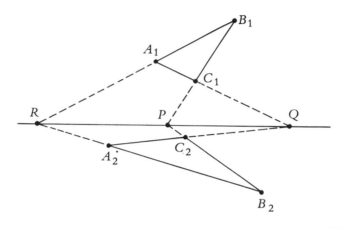

FIGURE 57

A convenient notation for keeping track of the incidences in the theorem of Desargues is the following.

$$A_1 - B_1 - C_1 - A_1$$

$$R \quad P \quad Q$$

$$A_2 - B_2 - C_2 - A_2$$

$$\overline{}$$

$$O$$

If one examines Figure 58 carefully, this notation should be self-explanatory.

An analytical proof of the theorem of Desargues will now be outlined. Let O be taken as the point $(1, 1, 1)$ and A_1, B_1, C_1 be the three points $(1, 0, 0)$, $(0, 1, 0)$, $(0, 0, 1)$. The equation of the line through O and A_1 is quickly found to be $x_2 = x_3$, hence a convenient representation for A_2 is $(a, 1, 1)$ with $a \neq 1$ so that A_2 is distinct from O. Likewise, we may take $B_2 = (1, b, 1)$ and

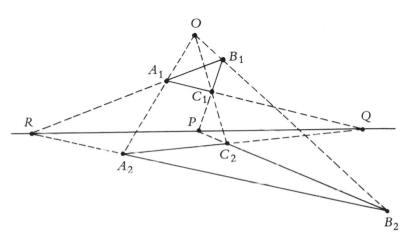

FIGURE 58

$C_2 = (1, 1, c)$ with $b \neq 1$, $c \neq 1$. There is an additional condition on a, b, and c that is necessary in order to assure that A_2, B_2 and C_2 are not collinear. We leave it to the reader to show that this condition is

$$abc + 2 - a - b - c \neq 0.$$

We next carry out analytically the details of the geometric construction which illustrates the theorem of Desargues. The reader will find that the equations of A_1B_1 and A_2B_2 are respectively $x_3 = 0$ and $(1 - b)x_1 + (1 - a)x_2 + (ab - 1)x_3 = 0$, and that their point of intersection R is $(a - 1, 1 - b, 0)$. Likewise, he will find P and Q to be $(0, b - 1, 1 - c)$ and $(a - 1, 0, 1 - c)$.

From

$$\begin{array}{ccccc} 0 & b-1 & 1-c & 0 & b-1 \\ a-1 & 0 & 1-c & a-1 & 0 \end{array}$$

the line coordinates of line PQ are found to be

$$[(b-1)(1-c),\ (1-c)(a-1),\ -(a-1)(b-1)].$$

To determine if $R = (a-1, 1-b, 0)$ is incident with line PQ, it is not necessary to write the equation of PQ. We merely inquire if the dot product condition for incidence, $u \cdot x = 0$, is satisfied. Since

$$(a-1)(b-1)(1-c) + (1-b)(1-c)(a-1) + 0$$
$$= (a-1)(b-1)(1-c) - (a-1)(b-1)(1-c) = 0$$

identically, we have shown that P, Q, and R are collinear.

An important result established in 1905 by Gerhard Hessenberg is that the theorem of Desargues can be proved merely by the repeated use of the theorem of Pappus. Because of the importance of this result in modern geometry, a modified version of Hessenberg's proof will be given.[†]

Let $A_1B_1C_1$ and $A_2B_2C_2$ in Figure 60 be two triangles that are perspective from O, and let pairs of their corresponding sides meet in points P, Q, R. We want to prove that P, Q, and R are collinear. To this end, we make the following constructions. The line A_1B_2 is drawn (dotted) and the intersection of this line with OC_1C_2 is labeled (D). The intersection of A_1C_1Q with B_2C_2P is labeled (E). The line EO is now drawn (also dotted) and its intersection with A_1B_1R is called (F) and with A_2B_2R is called (G). We next apply the theorem of Pappus to appropriate hexagons as indicated below.

[†] In this connection, see Pedoe *52*, Preface pp. xi, xii., and Chap. II.

$B_1\,C_2\,O\,E\,B_2\,A_1\,B_1$			$A_2\,C_2\,O\,E\,A_1\,B_2\,A_2$			$B_2\,E\,A_1\,F\,D\,G\,B_2$		
___	___	P	___	___	Q	___	___	P
___	___	D	___	___	D	___	___	Q
___	___	F	___	___	G	___	___	R

The first and second applications show the collinearity of PDF and QDG (dashed lines in Figure 59). The third application then uses these incidences to show the collinearity of PQR as desired.

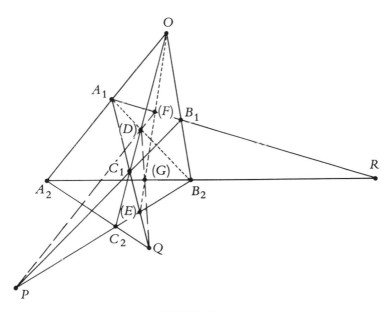

FIGURE 59

The converse of the theorem of Desargues is the following:

If two triangles are perspective from a line, they are perspective from a point.

Experimental construction for this converse would probably quickly lead the reader to suspect that the converse is a valid theorem. However, since the *converse* is exactly the *plane dual* of the theorem of Desargues, we know immediately—without the necessity of proof—that the converse theorem *is* valid. The converse theorem is sometimes included in the statement of the original theorem as follows:

If two triangles are perspective from a point (line), they are perspective from a line (point); or, If two triangles are perspective from a line, they are perspective from a point, and conversely.

As in the case of the theorem of Pappus, we leave to the reader the investigation of special and affine cases of the theorem of Desargues. The following are suggested:

1. Axis PQR passing through O but with O distinct from P, Q, R. This case is sometimes called the *minor* theorem of Desargues.[†]
2. Axis PQR passing through O with $O = R$ (i.e. O and R coinciding).
3. A_1, A_2, B_1, B_2 collinear.
4. $O = A$.   5. $O = A_1 = B_2$.   6. $A_1 = A_2$.
7. $A_1 = A_2, C_1 = C_2$.   8. A_2 on B_1C_1
9. A_1 on B_2C_2, A_2 on B_1C_1.
10. A_2 on B_1C_1, B_2 on A_1C_1, C_2 on A_1B_1
11. O the ideal point O^*, PQR an ordinary line.
12. O an ordinary point, PQR the ideal line $P^*Q^*R^*$.
13. O the ideal point O^*, PQR the ideal line $P^*Q^*R^*$.

Thus far in this section—as in all of our work dealing with the real projective plane—we have remained in the plane, i.e. we have not assumed that the plane was part of a more general space. It has

---

† See Blumenthal *12*, pp. 125, 134.

been this *isolation* of the plane from a surrounding space that has accounted for many of the modern developments in plane projective geometry.

On the other hand, in our intuitive approaches and when we have considered Euclidean or Cartesian affine models, we have not hesitated to use our knowledge of three-dimensional ordinary space as an aid and sometimes as a guide. Let us now consider two

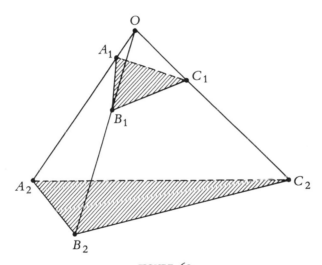

FIGURE 60

triangles in space that are perspective from an ordinary point (Figure 60). This point is evidently the vertex of the trihedral angle formed by the lines joining corresponding vertices of the triangles. In other words, our space figure can be thought of as a triangular pyramid, with $A_2B_2C_2$ as base and, for example, the points O, B_1, C_1, B_2, and C_2 all lying in one of the front faces. The triangle $A_1B_1C_1$ can then be thought of as a plane section of this pyramid. If we now raise the question of the validity of the theorem of Desargues in ordinary three-dimensional space, the answer is immediate and the theorem appears almost trivial. The points of intersection P, Q, R of B_1C_1 and B_2C_2, A_1C_1 and A_2C_2, A_1B_1 and A_2B_2 evidently all lie on the line which is the intersection of the planes containing the triangles $A_1B_1C_1$ and $A_2B_2C_2$ (Figure 61).

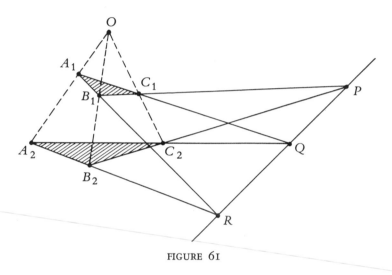

FIGURE 61

It would appear then that Figure 61 could be regarded either as a space or a plane figure (the latter being the projection of the space figure on a plane), and that hence we need not worry very much about a proof for the theorem of Desargues in the plane. This is the case if we think of the plane as being part of, or as being embedded in, a space of higher dimension. However, as we have indicated on page 101, it has been found fruitful to consider the projective plane as an entity by itself, entirely apart from any surrounding space. If one defines points as triples of real numbers, then the analytic proofs of the theorems of Pappus and Desargues that we have given are available for the real projective plane.

On the other hand if one proceeds synthetically in two dimensions, he starts with postulates of incidence. These may be the postulates that we have stated[†] or they may be some similar set.[‡] Since the theorems of Pappus and Desargues are nothing more than statements about the incidences of certain points and lines in the plane, it certainly would appear that these theorems should be consequences of whatever (consistent) set of incidence postulates is assumed.

Curiously enough this is not the case. As early as 1902, F. R. Moulton had devised a (quite simple) model of a projective plane, satisfying incidence postulates, in which the theorem of Desargues does not hold.[§] Such a plane is called non-Desarguesian. At this point we recall that the theorem of Desargues can be deduced from the theorem of Pappus. Hence, to form a set of postulates for a plane projective geometry in which these theorems always hold true, one method of procedure is merely to assume the theorem of Pappus as a postulate.[††]

Complete understanding of the significance and importance of the theorems of Pappus and Desargues has been reached only in comparatively recent times. Even a casual examination of such works as those by Blumenthal (*12*), Hall (*29* and *32*, Chapter 20), or by Skornyakov (*62*) will make it apparent that modern abstract algebra has been the key to this understanding.

Before leaving the theorem of Desargues, we call attention to a type of notation that is useful not only for this theorem but in many other situations in geometry. We begin by denoting any one of the points of the configuration of Desargues by the letter P

---

† See p. 47.

‡ See those of Menger, (used in Eves, *22*, p. 418).

§ See Eves *22*, p. 420 ff.

†† See those of Bachmann, used by Coxeter *19*, p. 229.

with two subscripts chosen from the first five integers, e.g. P_{12}.[†]
Any point collinear with P_{12} is denoted by using one of the subscripts 1 or 2 but with the other one replaced by a different integer. For example, let the second point be P_{13}. The third collinear point is now called P_{23} and the line containing these

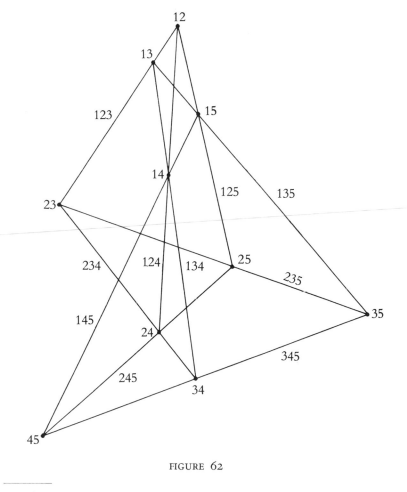

FIGURE 62

[†] The order of the integers is immaterial, i.e. $P_{12} = P_{21}$.

three points is called l_{123}. Next, a different point collinear with P_{12} is denoted say by P_{14}, the line of collinearity by l_{124} and the third point on this line by P_{24}. One now finds that the two points P_{15} and P_{25} on the third line l_{125} through P_{12} have their locations fixed, and that this is also the case with the remaining points. A further notational simplification comes by merely denoting the points and lines by their subscripts as in Figure 62.

The new notation will make it apparent that any one of the ten points of the Desargues configuration may be taken as the center of perspectivity, or any one of the ten lines as the axis of perspectivity, for some pair of triangles contained in the figure. In other words, the figure contains ten pairs of perspective triangles. The procedure for locating these in Figure 62 is as follows: Suppose the center of perspectivity is to be the point 34. Then each of the three vertices of one of the triangles will contain a 3 and each of the vertices of the other triangle a 4. Thus the two triangles are 13, 23, 35 and 14, 24, 45. The three integers that do not occur in the designation of the center of perspectivity give the axis, i.e., 125. The reader will doubtless want to practice in selecting and drawing additional sets of perspective triangles in the configuration.[24]

And finally we outline a project that some readers may want to check through in detail, whereas other readers will be content merely with the statement of results. Figure 63 is well worth some study however. Consider the complete 4-point with vertices $(1, 1, 1)$, $(-1, 1, 1)$, $(1, -1, 1)$, $(1, 1, -1)$. The diagonal triangle (see page 67) for this 4-point can be shown to be $(1, 0, 0)$, $(0, 1, 0)$, $(0, 0, 1)$. The six sides of the 4-point intersect the sides of its diagonal triangle (exclusive of the intersections at the diagonal points) in the six vertices of the complete 4-line $[1, 1, 1]$, $[-1, 1, 1]$, $[1, -1, 1]$, $[1, 1, -1]$. Thus the six vertices of the complete 4-line are on the sides of the complete 4-point, and the complete 4-point and the complete 4-line have a common diagonal triangle. The figure, minus the diagonal triangle, is a special configuration of Desargues and is self-dual. Notice that although the complete figure contains thirteen points and thirteen

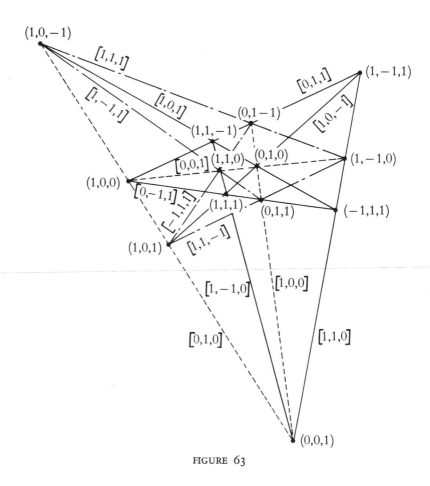

FIGURE 63

lines with many lines containing four points and many points having four lines passing through them, this is not true universally. Hence the figure is not a 13₄ configuration.

As metric specializations, the reader may be interested in drawing the above figure (1) when the four vertices of the complete 4-point are the vertices of a square, and (2) when they are the vertices and centroid of an equilateral triangle.

III.3   *The Theorems of Pascal and Brianchon*

In Section III.1 we inferred the following theorem which is known as the theorem of Pascal:

If the six (distinct) *vertices of a hexagon lie on a* (non-degenerate) *conic, then the three points of intersection of pairs of opposite sides are collinear* (on a line called the Pascal line of the hexagon).

We now proposed to outline an analytic proof for this theorem.

As the reader doubtless knows, the usual definitions of the curves known collectively as the conic sections involve the concept of distance, e.g. the parabola is defined as the locus of points equidistant from a fixed point and a fixed line not passing through the fixed point. Since the concept of distance is not a part of projective or affine geometries, a different approach must be used to define conics in these geometries. There are several ways of proceeding, but each of these requires too much preliminary detail to be considered here.[†] We shall merely state that, as the reader doubtless suspects, each of these approaches leads to a homogeneous equation of second degree in x_1, x_2, x_3 as the analytic description of a conic.

From our earlier proofs we realize that the algebraic work of our present proof will be greatly lessened by a judicious choice

---

[†] See Coxeter *18*, p. 87.

for the vertices of the hexagon. The following is found to be such a choice:

$$A = (0, r, -1) \quad C = (-1, 0, s) \quad E = (t, -1, 0)$$
$$B = (0, -1, r) \quad D = (s, 0, -1) \quad F = (-1, t, 0),$$

in which r, s, t are constants subject to certain restrictions that we shall determine shortly. The reader can quickly verify by direct substitution that these points lie on the conic with equation

$$x_1^2 + x_2^2 + x_3^2 + (r + 1/r)x_2x_3 + (s + 1/s)x_1x_3 + (t + 1/t)x_1x_2 = 0.$$

Thus for $A = (0, r, -1)$, we have

$$0 + r^2 + (-1)^2 + (r + 1/r)(r)(-1) + (s + 1/s)(0)(-1) +$$
$$(t + 1/t)(0)(r) = r^2 + 1 - r^2 - 1 = 0.$$

With these six points we form a hexagon $ABCDEF$ (Figure 64).

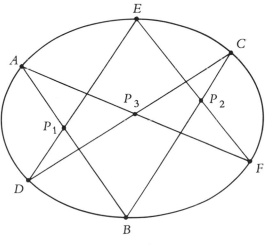

FIGURE 64

Then our earlier notation

	A	B	C	D	E	F	A	
		—			—			P_1
		—			—			P_2
		—			—			P_3

locates the points P_1, P_2, P_3 which are the points of intersection of pairs of opposite sides of the hexagon $ABCDEF$, and we now need to prove that P_1, P_2, P_3 are collinear.

However, before proceeding with our proof we should determine the restrictions that should be placed on the constants r, s, t in order that, for the general case, our points be distinct and the conic be non-degenerate. These turn out to be $r \neq 0$, $r \neq \pm 1$, $s \neq 0$, $s \neq \pm 1$, $t \neq 0$, $t \neq \pm 1$, $rs \neq t$, $rt \neq s$, $st \neq r$, $rst \neq 1$, and are determined in the following manner. The equation of the conic might have been written in a different form by multiplying each term by rst. In this form if we were to place $r = 0$, the entire equation would reduce to $x_2 x_3 = 0$ which represents a degenerate conic. Evidently if $r = +1$ or -1, A and B will be equivalent representations for the same point. Likewise for s and t. We next find the equation of say AD by our cross-product procedure. Starting with

$$\begin{array}{ccccc} 0 & r & -1 & 0 & r \\ s & 0 & -1 & s & 0 \end{array}$$

we find (in line coordinates)

$$AD = [-r, -s, -rs] \sim [r, s, rs]$$

and hence the equation of AD is

$$rx_1 + sx_2 + rsx_3 = 0.$$

We now see that if $F = (-1, t, 0)$ were collinear with A and D (thus causing the conic to degenerate), we would have

$$-r + st + (rs)(0) = 0, \quad \text{i.e. } st = r.$$

Likewise, the collinearity of, for example, D, B, and F takes place if and only if $rst = 1$. And so on for the other possibilities.

We now proceed with the proof and find P_1 as the intersection of lines AB and DE. The line coordinates for AB are found as follows. From

$$
\begin{array}{ccccc}
0 & r & -1 & 0 & r \\
0 & -1 & r & 0 & -1
\end{array}
$$

we have

$$AB = [r^2 - 1, 0, 0] \sim [1, 0, 0],$$

since $r \neq +1$. For DE, from

$$
\begin{array}{ccccc}
s & 0 & -1 & s & 0 \\
t & -1 & 0 & t & -1
\end{array}
$$

we obtain

$$DE = [-1, -t, -s] \sim [1, t, s].$$

Hence again using the cross-product procedure—this time for the point of intersection of AB and DE—we have

$$
\begin{array}{ccccc}
1 & 0 & 0 & 1 & 0 \\
1 & t & s & 1 & t
\end{array}
$$

and $P_1 = (0, -s, t)$. In similar fashion we obtain $P_2 = (r, -s, 0)$ and $P_3 = (r, 0, -t)$. The equation of $P_1 P_2$ is then found to be

$$stx_1 + trx_2 + rsx_3 = 0.$$

P_3 evidently lies on this line through P_1 and P_2 since the above equation is satisfied for $x_1 = r$, $x_2 = 0$, $x_3 = -t$.

The converse of Pascal's theorem can also be proved.

If the three points of intersection of pairs of opposite sides of a hexagon are collinear, then the six vertices of the hexagon lie on a conic.

As we have already seen, when the conic degenerates into a pair of straight lines we have the configuration of Pappus.

We shall shortly apply Pascal's theorem and its converse to several construction problems such as the following:

Problem 1. Given five points of a (point) conic A, B, C, D, E and a line l through one of these points, say C, find the second point X which the line l has in common with the conic (see Figure 65).

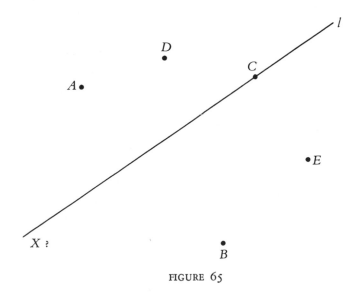

FIGURE 65

Before doing this, however, some preliminary remarks are in order.

First, the reader is reminded that in Section 1.4 we talked about point loci and also about line loci. For the present in this section we are thinking only about point conics. The theorem of Brianchon will deal with line conics.

Next, when we say "Given five points of a (point) conic ...," just what do we mean? The remainder of the problem above makes it clear that we do not mean that the entire conic is given; otherwise the problem would be nonsensical. This, then, raises the question, do five points (no three on a straight line, in order to avoid degenerate conics) always determine a unique conic? The answer is in the affirmative, but we shall not give the details here.[25]

Finally, the reader has doubtless observed that although Pascal's theorem is a theorem of projective geometry and as such is concerned with conics in general, we have illustrated the theorem with a particular conic, an ellipse. He must remember that it is not possible to visualize the projective plane (where the ideal points and line are to be indistinguishable from the ordinary points and lines) except at the expense of a completely new geometric interpretation of "point" and "line" such as we have given in Section II.2. Hence what is usually done is to illustrate projective theorems in the affine plane. In this plane, conics are classified according to their relationship with the ideal line of the plane which definitely is an exceptional line of the plane (one that we can't reach on the drawing board, so to speak). A conic that has no points incident with the ideal line is called an ellipse, one that has one point (or two "coincident" points) is called a parabola, and one that has two distinct points incident with the ideal line is called a hyperbola.† (The tangents to the hyperbola at its two ideal

---

† See Meserve *48*, p. 160.

points are asymptotes, and the tangent to the parabola at its ideal point is the ideal line.) Since all conics are projectively equivalent, we naturally select the ellipse (with no ideal points) as being the best one for a visual representation of a projective conic in the affine plane.

Referring back to problem 1 and to Figure 65, we note that line l can be written as the line through C and X, i.e. $l = CX$. From the schematic form useful for Pascal's theorem

$$A \quad B \quad C \quad X \quad D \quad E \quad A$$
$$\underline{\hspace{1cm}} \qquad \underline{\hspace{1cm}} \qquad\qquad P_1$$
$$\qquad \underline{\hspace{1cm}} \qquad \underline{\hspace{1cm}} \qquad P_2$$
$$\qquad \underline{\hspace{1cm}} \qquad\qquad \underline{\hspace{1cm}} \quad P_3$$

(note that X must be placed adjacent to C although it does not matter on which side), we can determine P_2 (as the intersection of BC and DE) and P_3 (as the intersection of l and EA). These two points determine the Pascal line which of course must contain P_1. But P_1 also lies on AB. Hence we have now located P_1, and since XD also passes through P_1, we can also construct XD. The desired point X lies both on this line and on l. Hence it must be the point of intersection of these two lines (see Figure 66).

It can be shown that the theorem of Pascal holds even when two (or three different pairs of) adjacent vertices coincide. If for example, B is moved around the conic until it coincides with A, it appears intuitively that the limiting position of the line through A and B will coincide with the tangent at A. This resulting special case of Pascal's theorem is sometimes stated as a separate theorem.

It the vertices of a pentagon lie on a point conic, then the tangent to the point conic at one of its vertices meets the side opposite that vertex at a point which is collinear with the points of intersection of the other two pairs of nonadjacent sides.

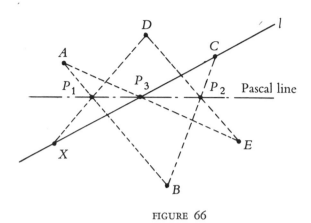

FIGURE 66

Likewise quadrangle or triangle theorems are obtained when two or three different pairs of vertices coincide. There is, however, no need even to state these special theorems as far as construction problems are concerned. To illustrate, let us consider a second problem:

Problem 2. Given five points of a conic, A, B, C, D, E, construct the tangent at one of them, say at A. Here we merely seek the line, a, which corresponds to the limiting position of the line through A and an adjacent point (of the hexagon) after the adjacent point has been made to coincide with A. Thus we can say that we are seeking $a = AA$, and write our schematic form as follows.

$$A \quad A \quad B \quad C \quad D \quad E \quad A$$

___		___				P_1
	___			___		P_2
		___			___	P_3

P_2 and P_3 are quickly constructed and hence the Pascal line can be drawn (Figure 67). The intersection of line CD with the Pascal line

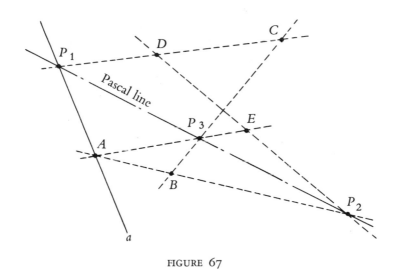

FIGURE 67

then locates point P_1, and finally the line through P_1 and A is
$AA = a$, the desired tangent at A.

We now consider the following affine problem:

Problem 3. Given one of the ideal points of an hyperbola, A^*,
and the tangents b and c at two ordinary points B and C, construct
an asymptote of the hyperbola (the tangent at A^*), i.e. given A^*,
$b = BB$, $c = CC$, construct $a = A^*A^*$.

From

A^*	A^*	B	B	C	C	A^*	
___			___				P_1
	___				___		P_2
		___			___		P_3

we construct P_2, the intersection of A^*B (the line parallel to the
one giving the direction of A^* through B) and c (Figure 68). Next
we construct P_3, the intersection of b and CA^* to obtain the Pascal

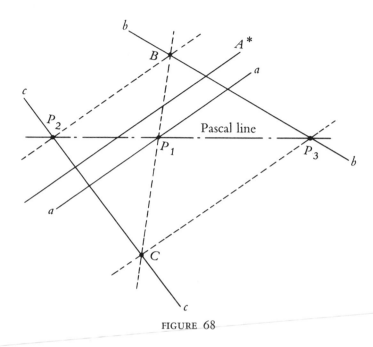

FIGURE 68

line. We now find P_1 as the intersection of the Pascal line and BC. Drawing a line through P_1 parallel to the direction of A^*, we have the desired asymptote $a = A^* A^*$.

We now state (without proof because a proof is unnecessary) the dual of Pascal's theorem which was discovered many years later by Brianchon.

If the six sides of a hexagon are tangents to a conic, then the three lines joining pairs of opposite vertices are concurrent (at a point called the Brianchon point of the hexagon).

Let us call the tangent lines a, b, c, d, e, f. Then the lines l_1, l_2, l_3, joining pairs of opposite vertices, can be located from the following schematic arrangement.

a	b	c	d	e	f	a	
—		—					l_1
	—			—			l_2
			—		—		l_3

In Figure 69, instead of trying to draw a large number of lines of a line conic (which is of course what we are dealing with here), we have merely drawn the six tangent lines to a (dotted) point conic.

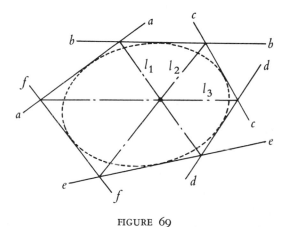

FIGURE 69

A single construction problem will be solved to indicate possible uses of Brianchon's theorem:

Problem 4. Let a (line) conic be given by three tangent lines and the points of contact on two of them. Construct the point of contact on the third line. That is, given a, b, c, and $A = aa$, $B = bb$, construct $C = cc$.

Using

a	a	b	b	c	c	a	
—		—					l_1
	—			—			l_2
			—		—		l_3

we first construct l_1 and l_3, thus locating the Brianchon point. Then the intersection of c with l_2, the line through the Brianchon point and the intersection of a and b, gives the desired point of contact, $C = cc$, on line c (Figure 70).

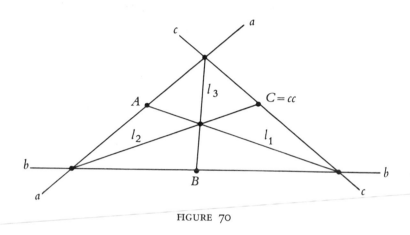

FIGURE 70

The four problems that we have solved are probably sufficient to indicate the variety of construction problems concerned with conics that can easily be solved on the drawing board with the aid of Pascal's and Brianchon's theorems. The reader who wants more of them will find 102 additional problems suggested in Patterson *51*, pp. 265–66.

What may not be apparent to the reader is that these geometric constructions afford approximate solutions to problems, encountered for example in the aircraft industry, that are exceedingly burdensome when tackled by analytic means.[†]

† See R. A. Liming, *Practical Analytic Geometry with Applications to Aircraft* (New York: Macmillan, 1944), and L. J. Adams, and P. A. White, *Analytic Geometry and Calculus* (New York: Oxford University Press, 1961), p. 282.

No writer discussing the Pascal theorem can resist giving a brief introduction to what is usually called the *mystic hexagram* but which might better be called the *complete Pascal figure*. In constructing the picture for the proof of the Pascal theorem concerned with the six points A, B, C, D, E, F, we joined these points in the alphabetical order to obtain the hexagon $ABCDEF$. We might have joined them in any of $5!/2 = 60$ different orders. Thus there are 60 different hexagons[26] given by six distinct points of a (nondegenerate) conic, and they generate 60 different Pascal lines. The incidences of these 60 lines, together with the additional lines and points to which they give rise, have been studied by many writers since the time of J. Steiner (1796–1863). We shall try to summarize this *complete Pascal figure*. It consists of:

60 Pascal lines h and 60 Kirkman points H,
20 Cayley-Salmon lines g and 20 Steiner points G,
15 Steiner-Plücker lines i and 15 Salmon lines I.
On each h line lie three H points and one G point,
on each g line lie three H points, three I points, and one G point, and
on each i line lie four G points.
Through each H point pass three h lines and one g line,
through each G point pass three h lines, three i lines, and one g line, and
through each I point pass four g lines.

These incidences can be represented schematically as in Figure 71.

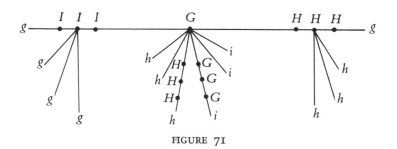

FIGURE 71

Admittedly, what we have stated thus far is probably very difficult for the reader to comprehend and impossible for him to visualize. If he is lucky enough to have access to a large university library, he may be able to locate the thesis of Anne and Elizabeth Linton (*Pascal's Mystic Hexagram*, Philadelphia, 1921) which contains some very interesting drawings of the hexagram.[27] But there is more to the complete Pascal figure than we have so far described.

The Pascal line for the hexagon $ABCDEF$ (see Figure 65) contains the three constructed points P_1, P_2, and P_3 which can be called the Pascal points for that hexagon. When all 60 of the Pascal lines are constructed, it turns out that there are only 45 distinct Pascal points. Four Pascal lines pass through each of these Pascal points and thus the figure consisting of only the Pascal lines and points is a 45_3 60_4 configuration.

Furthermore:

> *The 60 Pascal lines can be divided into six sets of ten, meeting in threes in ten Kirkman points, of which three lie on any one of the Pascal lines; the configuration in each of the partial figures is that of two triangles in perspective with their center and axis of perspectivity.*[†]

Thus the component part of the complete Pascal figure is none other than our old friend, the configuration of Desargues, i.e. the $(10_3)_1$.

[†] Baker 7, p. 355.

IV

The General
Projective Plane
and
Finite Projective Planes

IV.1   *Postulates for the General Projective Plane*

Most Americans know that there are many able Soviet mathematicians. The idea persists, in some quarters, that these Soviet mathematicians are all working in applied mathematics. Partly to dispel this notion, as well as for its intrinsic interest, we begin this section with a quotation from the Soviet mathematician L. A. Skornyakov.

> *At the present time it is a common practice to adjoin to the ordinary Euclidean plane* ideal *or* infinitely remote *points which form an ideal or* infinitely remote *line. In this way uniformity in the statements and proof of a succession of theorems in analytic geometry and in several other branches of geometry is achieved. ... this procedure leads to the construction of classical projective geometry. With the development of the axiomatic method various descriptions of projective spaces were constructed ....*

> *Further investigations showed that geometrical systems subject only to axioms of incidence have independent significance and their theory turned out to be very profound. Thus it has become customary to understand by a projective space just such a geometrical system.*
>
> *In projective spaces of dimension two, i.e. projective planes, the theorem of Desargues may not hold and the above mentioned reduction to algebra [omitted from this quotation] is not successful in the general case. The study of projective planes is also independently of interest and their theory has been successfully developed since the beginning of the present century. Notable results in this field have been obtained during the last two decades. In recent years Soviet mathematicians have interested themselves in these questions and have already achieved considerable success.*[†]

The impetus for much of the work done in recent years in the areas mentioned by Skornyakov comes from a 1943 paper by M. Hall.[‡] The pioneering work, however, was done by Veblen and others about the beginning of the present century.

To characterize the projective plane, Hall uses only the postulates

P1 Exactly one line is incident with every two distinct points,

P2 Exactly one point is incident with every two distinct lines,

that we have discussed in Section II.I. He later added a third postulate,

P3 There exist four distinct points, no three of which are contained in one line,[§]

in order to rule out certain trivial cases discussed in *29* and called *degenerate planes* by Skornyakov.[††]

[†] *62*, pp. 52, 55.
[‡] Hall *29*. See also *30, 31, 32*.
[§] *30*, p. 346.
[††] *62*, p. 57.

We have already shown the consistency of postulates P1 and P2 by means of our model in the real projective plane. Points $(1, 0, 0)$, $(0, 1, 0)$, $(0, 0, 1)$, $(1, 1, 1)$ of that plane satisfy the requirements in postulate P3, and hence P1, P2 and P3 form a consistent set of postulates.

We note that nothing in postulates P1, P2, P3 guarantees an unlimited number of points and lines. In fact, postulate P3 strongly hints that there are such things as *finite projective planes*, i.e. projective planes with only a finite number of points and lines. We shall discuss these in the next section.

First, perhaps we should call attention (as does Blumenthal *12*, p. 110) to the fact that the points and lines mentioned in the above postulates do not have to be geometric entities. We can start with any abstract set whose elements are called points and are denoted by capital letters A, B, ... , and any other abstract set whose elements are called lines and are denoted by lower-case letters a, b, ... The relation called incidence can be defined subject to the additional postulates

P4 If P denotes a point and l denotes a line, and P is incident with l, then l is incident with P,

P5 If l denotes a line and P denotes a point, and l is incident with P, then P is incident with l.

It can be shown that postulates P1, P2, P3 imply the following. There exist four (distinct) lines, no three of which pass through the same point. The "principle of duality" is thus a built-in feature of the general projective plane.[†]

[†] It is stated as a theorem and then proved in Ryser *58*, p. 90.

IV.2 *Definitions, Basic Theorem, and an Example*

As we mentioned on page 47, different kinds of projective planes can be generated analytically by restricting the numbers that we use for x_1, x_2, x_3 to particular sets or classes of numbers. Up to the present we have permitted x_1, x_2, x_3 to be any real numbers, and thus we have been dealing with real projective geometry. We shall now restrict the underlying number set to a finite collection of numbers which will then generate only a finite number of points. An example will be given shortly, but first we state some definitions and a basic theorem.

A projective plane is called *finite* if it contains only a finite number of points. Such planes are very important in combinatorial mathematics and have many applications. If the total number of points on a line of a finite plane is $n + 1$, then the positive integer n is called the *order* of the plane.

One of the basic theorems of finite planes is the following.

Let π be a finite projective plane of order n. Then the total number of points on an arbitrary line of π as well as the total number of lines through an arbitrary point of π are each equal to $n + 1$. Moreover, π has a totality of $n^2 + n + 1$ points and $n^2 + n + 1$ lines.[†]

Finite planes are thus $(n^2 + n + 1)_{n+1}$ configurations.

Let us now try to generate a finite plane by taking only those points that can be defined using the integers 0 and 1.[28] We quickly find that there will be exactly seven of these points. (At first sight it might appear that the number would be eight i.e. two choices for each of the x_1, x_2, x_3, but then we remember

---

[†] This theorem is proved in Ryser *58*, p. 91, as well as in most of the other references to these planes. See also Veblen and Young *67*, Intro.

that the 0, 0, 0 triple cannot be used.) These seven points are the following: $P_1(0, 1, 1)$, $P_2(1, 1, 1)$, $P_3(1, 0, 0)$, $P_4(0, 1, 0)$, $P_5(0, 0, 1)$, $P_6(1, 0, 1)$, $P_7(1, 1, 0)$.

The theorem stated above tells us that the totality of points of a finite plane of order n is $n^2 + n + 1$. Since 7 can be written as $2^2 + 2 + 1$, a finite plane having seven points would be of order 2. Thus according to the theorem, such a plane would contain seven lines and would have $n + 1 = 3$ points on each line and three lines through each point and hence be equivalent to the 7_3 configuration whose configuration table is given on page 74. Taking point P_1 as the point called 1 in this table, P_2 the point called 2 etc., we now write the equations of six lines of the configuration following the order we used when we attempted to "realize" the 7_3 configuration in Euclidean plane geometry (see page 75). We omit the details of finding these equations, but one can quickly check by direct substitution that they are the following:

$$P_1P_2P_3: \quad x_2 - x_3 = 0,$$
$$P_1P_4P_5: \quad x_1 = 0,$$
$$P_2P_4P_6: \quad x_1 - x_3 = 0,$$
$$P_3P_5P_6: \quad x_2 = 0,$$
$$P_3P_4P_7: \quad x_3 = 0.$$

From the table, points P_1, P_6, P_7 should also be collinear. We find the equation of P_1P_6 as follows.

$$
\begin{array}{ccccc}
0 & 1 & 1 & 0 & 1 \\
1 & 0 & 1 & 1 & 0
\end{array}
$$

$$P_1P_6 = [1, 1, -1], \quad \text{i.e. } x_1 + x_2 - x_3 = 0.$$

Line P_1P_6 obviously is not incident with $P_7 = (1, 1, 0)$ since $1 + 1 - 0 \neq 0$. Hence points P_1, P_6, P_7 do not lie on a line in real projective geometry. We can, however, make a model for our projective plane of order 2, i.e. for the 7_3 configuration, in which six of the columns of the configuration table do correspond to straight lines but in which the seventh "line" is represented by, for example, the dotted circle in Figure 72.[29]

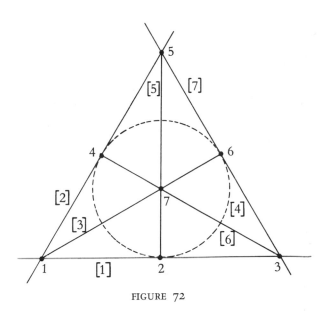

FIGURE 72

IV.3   *An Unsettled Issue*

The projective plane of order 2 is the "smallest" projective plane, since one of order 1 would contain only three points and thus would not satisfy postulate P3. An immediate question that arises is the following: Is there a finite projective plane of the order n for each positive integer $n \geq 2$? The answer to this question is in the negative, but "The determination of the precise range of values of n is one of the major unsettled issues in combinatorics today. The first undecided case is $n = 10$."[†] We shall shortly give a chart showing the status for $n = 2, 3, \ldots, 19$, but first we give the statements of some known results.

In 1906, O. Veblen and W. H. Bussey showed that there exists a finite projective plane or order n whenever n is a prime or a power of a prime. Hence, there are infinitely many positive integers n which are orders of finite projective planes. No others are known, but so far there has been no general proof that these are the only possible ones.

The solution of a seemingly unrelated problem by G. Tarry in 1901 showed that there is no finite projective plane of order 6. However, not until 1949 was the nonexistence for other orders proved. In that year R. H. Bruck and H. J. Ryser (*13*) were able to find infinitely many values of n for which there is no finite projective plane. Their theorem may be stated as follows:

If n is 1 or 2 more than a multiple of 4 and if it contains to an odd power some prime factor which is 1 less than a mulitple of 4, there is no finite projective plane of order n.

Thus, since $6 = 2 \cdot 3$ and 3 is a prime factor (raised to an odd power 1) which is one less than the first multiple of 4, Tarry's result is checked. The next value of n to which this theorem applies is $14 = 2 \cdot 7$, where 7 is a prime factor to an odd power and is one less than two times 4.

The theorem of Desargues (including the special cases when one, two, or three vertices of one triangle lie on the sides of the other triangle) has been proved to be a true theorem in the real projective plane. Does this theorem or its special cases hold in the

---

[†] Ryser *58*, p. 94.

Order $(=n)$	Existence	Number of points (lines) $= n^2 + n + 1$	Number of points (lines) on a line (point) $= n + 1$	Type
2	Yes	7	3	Only the Desarguesian plane exists.
3	Yes	13	4	Only the Desarguesian plane exists.
4	Yes	21	5	Only the Desarguesian plane exists.
5	Yes	31	6	Only the Desarguesian plane exists.
6	No	Non-existence proved by Tarry in 1901.		
7	Yes	57	8	Only the Desarguesian plane exists.
8	Yes	73	9	Only the Desarguesian plane exists.
9	Yes	91	10	Non-Desarguesian planes exist.
10	?			
11	Yes	133	12	Only the Desarguesian plane is known.
12	?			
13	Yes	183	14	Only the Desarguesian plane is known.
14	No	Non-existence proved by Bruck and Ryser in 1949		
15	?			
16	Yes	273	17	Non-Desarguesian planes exist.
17	Yes	307	18	Only the Desarguesian plane is known.
18	?			
19	Yes	421	20	Only the Desarguesian plane is known.

FIGURE 73. FINITE PLANES

finite planes? If so, the plane is called Desarguesian, if not, non-Desarguesian. For $n = 2, 3, \ldots, 8$, it has been shown that only the Desarguesian planes exist, but for $n = 9$, in addition to the Desarguesian, several non-Desarguesian planes have been found. Their existence has also been proved for $n = p^r$, p odd, $r \geq 2$, and for $n = 2^{2s}$, $s \geq 2$. For $n = p$ only the Desarguesian plane is known. The summary for $n = 2, 3, \ldots, 19$ is shown in the form of a table (Figure 73).

We close this section by describing a procedure that can be used to form the incidence table for a finite plane, i.e. an $(n^2 + n + 1)_{n+1}$ configuration. We should probably first remind ourselves of the make-up of these tables. With the first n positive integers representing the $n^2 + n + 1$ points, and the columns of the table—each with $n + 1$ integers—representing the lines, we see that (1) there must be no duplication of integers in any column (since each line must contain $n + 1$ *distinct* points); (2) two different columns cannot have a pair of integers in common (otherwise the corresponding lines would coincide); and (3) every integer must occur exactly $n + 1$ times (since every point is incident with $n + 1$ lines). Let us illustrate the procedure mentioned at the beginning of this paragraph by finding the incidence table for the finite plane of order 3, i.e. for the 13_4 configuration. The general case is discussed in Wesson (*69*).

With $n = 3$, we have $n^2 + n + 1 = 13$ points—which will be represented by the integers 1, 2, ..., 13. Since $n + 1 = 4$, we must use each of these integers four times in forming the table. Place one of them, say the 1 in each of the first four spaces of the first row; then complete the first four columns with the remaining integers 2, 3, ... , 13 in order. Next, place 2's in the fifth, sixth, and seventh spaces of the first row, followed by three 3's and three 4's. We have now exhausted our supply of 1's, 2's and 3's, and the table looks as follows:

```
1  1   1   1     2   2   2      3   3   3      4   4   4
2  5   8  11
3  6   9  12
4  7  10  13
```

To complete—in an orderly fashion—the columns headed by the 2's we can use the integers 5, 6, ..., 13 in sequence, but this time spreading them out by rows instead of by columns. The integers 5, 6, and 7 can also be used for the second row of the column headed by 3's and 4's without violating any of our conditions. The table now appears as follows where the last 3 by 3 arrays have been enclosed in boxes for purposes of reference.

```
1  1   1   1     2   2   2      3   3   3      4   4   4
2  5   8  11    | 5   6   7 |  | 5   6   7 |  | 5   6   7 |
3  6   9  12    | 8   9  10 |  |           |  |           |
4  7  10  13    |11  12  13 |  |           |  |           |
```

The last two (uncompleted) arrays can be completed by satisfying the following conditions: (1) each row of each array must contain the same integers as the corresponding row of the completed array; (2) each of the integers 8, 9, ..., 13 is to be in a different column in each array; and (3) there should be one column in each of the last two arrays that contains any two integers from different rows of the completed array. This sounds like puzzle-solving, and that is essentially what this procedure reduces to, i.e. trying one by one a finite number of possibilities.

It does not take many trials in the case of the 13_4 to discover that the last two arrays can be completed with

$$\begin{array}{ccc} 9 & 10 & 8 \\ 13 & 11 & 12 \end{array} \quad \text{and} \quad \begin{array}{ccc} 10 & 8 & 9 \\ 12 & 13 & 11 \end{array}$$

in either order. One can easily imagine, however, that for larger values of n, this procedure leaves considerable to be desired. We shall have some better methods of forming incidence tables in later sections.[30]

IV.4 *Finite Projective Planes and Latin Squares*

We begin this section with some remarks on the topic of *Latin squares*—a topic that is frequently considered to be a part of recreational mathematics (although there are important applications)[31] and that, at first sight, appears to have no connection with finite planes.

An n-sided Latin square can be considered to be an arrangement of the first n positive integers into n rows and n columns in such a way that no row and no column contains any particular integer twice. The *order* of the Latin square is defined to be n. Two Latin squares are said to be *orthogonal* if when one is superposed upon the other, every ordered pair of numbers appears once in the resulting square.

For $n = 2$,

$$
\begin{array}{cc}
1 & 2 \\
2 & 1
\end{array}
$$

is a Latin square and it is the only Latin square of that order, i.e. there is no other Latin square of order 2 that is orthogonal to this one. On the other hand for $n = 3$, the squares

$$
\begin{array}{ccc}
1 & 2 & 3 \\
3 & 1 & 2 \\
2 & 3 & 1
\end{array}
\qquad
\begin{array}{ccc}
1 & 2 & 3 \\
2 & 3 & 1 \\
3 & 1 & 2
\end{array}
$$

are quickly seen to be orthogonal when one superposes the second on the first (by writing the elements of the second square to the right of those in the first square to form ordered pairs in the resulting square as shown below).

$$
\begin{array}{ccc}
11 & 22 & 33 \\
32 & 13 & 21 \\
23 & 31 & 12
\end{array}
$$

Various methods have been devised for the construction of sets of orthogonal squares, but as yet no method has been given that would yield all possible sets of them. It has been shown that for a given n, $n - 1$ is the maximum number of mutually orthogonal Latin squares. Such a set is said to be *complete*. Thus the two Latin squares given above form a complete set of orthogonal squares of order 3.

Using results from a part of mathematics known as *Galois fields*, it is possible to prove that if $n = p^\alpha$, where p is a prime and α is a positive integer, then for $n \geq 3$ there exists a complete set of $n - 1$ orthogonal Latin squares of order n. Thus we know that these sets exist for $n = 3$, $4 = 2^2$, 5, 7, $8 = 2^3$, $9 = 3^2$, 11, 13, etc.

R. C. Bose and W. L. Stevens have shown independently that the existence of a finite projective plane with $n + 1$ points per line is equivalent to the existence of a set of completely orthogonal n-by-n Latin squares. With no attempt at justification, we shall now try to explain a procedure that can be used to complete, with the aid of sets of completely orthogonal Latin squares, the tables for finite planes that were started in the preceding section.

We recopy the (incomplete) table for the 13_4 from page 130.

```
1  1   1   1        2   2   2        3  3  3        4  4  4
2  5   8  11        5   6   7        5  6  7        5  6  7
3  6   9  12        8   9  10
4  7  10  13       11  12  13
```

where the completed and uncompleted 3-by-3 arrays are again
enclosed in squares. We also recopy the complete orthogonal set
of Latin squares of order 3.

```
1  2  3        1  2  3
3  1  2        2  3  1
2  3  1        3  1  2
```

The columns of an incomplete 3-by-3 array of the table may now
be completed by looking in the completed array for those integers
which occupy the spaces corresponding to those spaces in the
Latin squares where the *same* symbol occurs.

For example in the first Latin square the same symbol, 1, occurs
in each of the spaces of the diagonal position extending from upper
left to lower right. The corresponding spaces in the completed
array are occupied by the integers 5, 9, 13. Therefore 5, 9, 13
becomes the first column in one of the incomplete arrays. Likewise, since the symbol 2 in the first Latin square occupies the

spaces indicated by circles in the accompanying square, we look
for the integers in these corresponding locations in the completed

array and find 6, 10, 11. Hence, we have the second column of the array we are completing. Doing the same thing for the symbol 3, we find 7, 8, 12 as the third column. We then use the second Latin square and the same process to complete the second in-complete array.

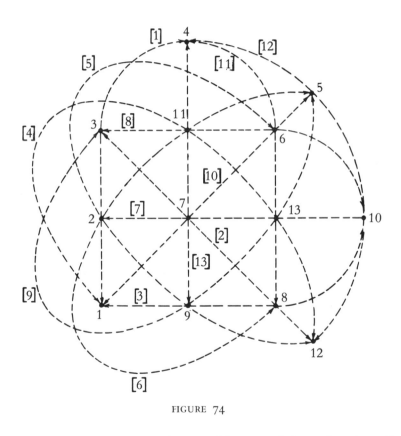

FIGURE 74

It would be interesting if we could now exhibit a drawing of our finite plane of order 3 with the points and lines labeled as follows:

[1]	[2]	[3]	[4]	[5]	[6]	[7]	[8]	[9]	[10]	[11]	[12]	[13]
1	1	1	1	2	2	2	3	3	3	4	4	4
2	5	8	11	5	6	7	5	6	7	5	6	7
3	6	9	12	8	9	10	9	10	8	10	8	9
4	7	10	13	11	12	13	13	11	12	12	13	11

Unfortunately, the 13_4 configuration cannot be "realized" in the real projective (or affine) plane. The best we can do is to give a schematic figure (Figure 74).

IV.5   *The Euler Conjecture*

Leonhard Euler (1707–83), the great Swiss mathematician, proposed the following problem. Each of six different regiments has six officers, one belonging to each of six different ranks. Can these 36 officers be arranged in a square formation so that each row and each column of this formation contains one officer of each rank and one from each regiment? We can label the ranks and regiments from 1 through 6 and assign to each officer an ordered pair of numbers, the first designating his rank and the second his regiment. The problem then reduces to the construction of a pair of orthogonal Latin squares of order 6.

By 1772, Euler was firmly convinced that it was not possible to have a pair of orthogonal Latin squares of order 6. In this he was correct (proved by Tarry in 1901), but unfortunately, he went further. He conjectured that there does not exist a pair of orthogonal Latin squares of order $n = 4k + 2$ for any positive integer k. Substituting $k = 1$ gives $n = 6$. The next case ($k = 2$) makes $n = 10$. It has long been realized that this case could not be decided by paper-and-pencil trials, and it has appeared to be even beyond the range of modern high-speed computers. In 1955,

Hall reported, "For $n = 10$, extensive searches on the SWAC machine at UCLA have failed to produce any orthogonal squares. But even 100 machine hours will not cover more than a microscopic part of the complete search."[†]

In an age when computers appear to be dominant and when not only the average man, but also the average mathematician, has become somewhat intimidated by them, it is refreshing to report that in 1959, three mathematicians—E. T. Parker, R. C. Bose, and S. S. Shrikhande—demolished Euler's conjecture apparently without the use of computing machines.

Specifically, they not only found two orthogonal Latin squares of order 10 but they proved the existence of such pairs for all the additional values of n for which Euler conjectured that they did not exist. A very readable account of this discovery has been written by Martin Gardner (*26*), including the exhibition of the squares of order 10. A special case of the general result is discussed by Ryser (*58*, pp. 85–89).

Evidently obtaining *two* orthogonal Latin squares of order 10 is a long way from obtaining the complete set of nine that is required to prove the existence of a finite projective plane of order 10. However, what might be called a revolutionary discovery has been made, and who knows what lies ahead? Writing the Preface to his *Combinatorial Mathematics* in 1963, Ryser has said, "Combinatorial mathematics is tremendously alive at this moment, and we believe that its greatest truths are still to be revealed."[‡] Ryser should be considered a prophet not without honor since in 1955 he said:

For $n = 10$, there are something like $2^{10,000}$ possible candidates for an

---

[†] *31*, p. 21.
[‡] *58*, p. x.

incidence matrix. [An incidence matrix can be considered to be a form of incidence table.] Machines cannot cope with numbers of this magnitude. But the right combination of computation and theory will continue to produce worthwhile results.[†]

IV.6   Finite Projective Planes and Perfect Difference Sets

Once again we begin a section by giving a brief discussion of a topic—perfect difference sets—that appears to have no connection with finite planes. One way of defining a perfect difference set of order n is to say that $n + 1$ integers $d_1, d_2, ..., d_{n+1}$ form such a set if their $n^2 + n$ differences $d_i - d_j$, where i and j each take all of the values 1, 2, ..., $n + 1$ but with $i \neq j$, are simply plus or minus the first $(n^2 + n)/2$ positive integers in some order. For $n = 2$, the integers 1, 2, 4 form a perfect difference set since $1 - 2 = -1$, $1 - 4 = -3$, $2 - 4 = -2$, $2 - 1 = 1$, $4 - 1 = 3$ $4 - 2 = 2$.

In what is now referred to as a "classical" paper (published in 1938), Singer (63) has shown that the sufficient condition for the existence of a perfect difference set is that n be a prime or the power of a prime; that the construction of perfect difference sets is precisely equivalent to the construction of what are called *cyclic* finite projective planes (to be defined in terms of an example presently); and that every finite Desarguesian plane is cyclic. No finite Desarguesian planes have been found that are not cyclic, and H. B. Mann and T. A. Evans have shown that for a cyclic plane and for $n \leq 1600$, we must have n equal to a prime or the power of a prime.

[†] 57, p. 30.

The following table displays perfect difference sets for the first few values of n.

n	Perfect difference set
2	1, 2, 4
3	1, 2, 4, 10
$4 = 2^2$	1, 2, 5, 15, 17
5	1, 2, 4, 9, 13, 19
6	None
7	1, 2, 4, 14, 33, 37, 44, 53
$8 = 2^3$	1, 2, 4, 8, 16, 32, 37, 55, 64
$9 = 3^2$	1, 2, 4, 10, 28, 50, 57, 62, 78, 82
10	?
11	1, 2, 4, 13, 21, 35, 39, 82, 89, 95, 105, 110
12	?

We now exhibit the incidence table for the cyclic finite plane of order 2 that is formed from the perfect difference set 1, 2, 4. It is

$$
\begin{array}{ccccccc}
1 & 2 & 3 & 4 & 5 & 6 & 7 \\
2 & 3 & 4 & 5 & 6 & 7 & 1 \\
4 & 5 & 6 & 7 & 1 & 2 & 3
\end{array}
$$

Such tables for planes of order n are evidently very easy to write down when one knows a perfect difference set of order n, and it would appear that we could use a perfect difference set of order n to first define the incidence table for a finite projective plane of order n and then, by reversing the procedure of the last section, use the incidence table to form an $n-1$ complete orthogonal set of n-by-n Latin squares. We illustrate this for $n = 4$.

From the perfect difference set 1, 2, 5, 15, 17 we form the incidence table for the 21₅,

```
 1  2  3  4  5  6  7  8  9 10 11 12 13 14 15 16 17 18 19 20 21
 2  3  4  5  6  7  8  9 10 11 12 13 14 15 16 17 18 19 20 21  1
 5  6  7  8  9 10 11 12 13 14 15 16 17 18 19 20 21  1  2  3  4
15 16 17 18 19 20 21  1  2  3  4  5  6  7  8  9 10 11 12 13 14
17 18 19 20 21  1  2  3  4  5  6  7  8  9 10 11 12 13 14 15 16
```

and then rearrange it as follows:

```
 1  1  1  1  1    2  2  2  2      5  5  5  5     15 15 15 15     17 17 17 17
 2  6  3 18 16    6  7 10 20      6  7 10 20      6  7 10 20      6  7 10 20
 5  7  8 11 21    3  8  9 12      9 12  3  8     12  9  8  3      8  3 12  9
15 10  9 13  4   18 11 13 19     19 13 11 18     11 18 19 13     13 19 18 11
17 20 12 19 14   16 21  4 14     21 16 14  4      4 14 16 21     14  4 21 16
```

Taking the first column of the second square array, 6, 9, 19, 21, we locate the spaces of the first square array that are occupied by these integers. They are located as follows:

We now place the same symbol (1 is a convenient one) in each of these spaces and repeat the operation. When we have completed the process for the second, third, and fourth arrays, we have generated the following complete orthogonal set of Latin squares of order 4.

1	2	3	4
3	4	1	2
4	3	2	1
2	1	4	3

1	2	3	4
4	3	2	1
2	1	4	3
3	4	1	2

1	2	3	4
2	1	4	3
3	4	1	2
4	3	2	1

Starting with the perfect difference set for $n = 5$, the reader can try his hand at generating the orthogonal set of Latin squares of order 5. (They are given in Gardner 26. The complete set for $n = 9$ is found in Pickert 54, p. 293).

This final chapter has considered a number of topics that at first sight appeared to be unrelated to each other. However, closer examination will reveal underlying connections. The chapter has been designed to show that present-day mathematicians are actively engaged in extending earlier classical results in new and far-reaching directions.

For the book as a whole, a fairly strict application of the "Penguin Principle"—mentioned in the Preface—has ruled out many topics that might have been included. The objective of the book will have been attained if the reader feels that he has broadened his horizon as far as geometry is concerned. If he desires to make a more intensive study of the subject, the bibliography will supply him with the titles of many excellent texts.

Notes

1. There are many books that discuss non-Euclidean geometry. Some of them are highly technical, others are very readable. We give only the following two references, each of which stresses the historical development of the subject: Blumenthal *12*, Chap. 1, and Wolfe *71*.

2. For example, see Adler *1*, Chap. 11, or Delachet *21*, Part I, or Eves and Newsom *23*, pp. 134–37, or Meserve *48*. The fundamental transformations of plane Euclidean geometry are discussed by synthetic methods in Yaglom *73* and in Perfect *53*.

3. See Blumenthal *11*, p. 5, or Eves and Newsom *23*, pp. 245–51, or Maurice Fréchet, "Abstract Sets, Abstract Spaces and General Analysis," Chap. 20 of James (ed.) *38*. (Fréchet is generally credited with having inaugurated the study of abstract spaces.)

4. As an indication of the continued usefulness and importance of Klein's classification, we quote the following sentences from the Preface to Levy *46*, *Projective and Related Geometries* (1964).

> *I have adopted Klein's formulation of geometry as the invariant theory of a given set under a given group of transformations, and I have developed this point of view consistently and systematically . . . . There are many advantages . . . in this type of development.*

5. A reasonably careful definition of a *homeomorphism* or *topological transformation* is that it is a transformation which is continuous and has a continuous inverse transformation. For those readers with the proper mathematical background we state that the analytic form of such a transformation, if "differentiable," is

$$x' = f(x, y)$$
$$y' = g(x, y)$$

where $f(x, y)$ and $g(x, y)$ are single-valued and continuous and where

$$\begin{vmatrix} \dfrac{\delta f}{\delta x} & \dfrac{\delta f}{\delta y} \\[2ex] \dfrac{\delta g}{\delta x} & \dfrac{\delta g}{\delta y} \end{vmatrix} \neq 0.$$

6. Why can a topologist be described as "a man who doesn't know the difference between a doughnut and a coffee cup"? See Mansfield *47*, p. 1.

7. The transformation group of plane projective point geometry is the totality of all transformations of the form

$$x' = (ax + by + c)/(gx + hy + i)$$
$$y' = (dx + ey + f)/(gx + hy + i),$$

where $a, b, c, \ldots$ are any real numbers satisfying the condition

$$\begin{vmatrix} a & b & c \\ d & e & f \\ g & h & i \end{vmatrix} \neq 0.$$

8. For further introduction to projective geometry, read Kline *42*,

Chap. XI, which is entitled "Science Born of Art: Projective Geometry."

9. See Eves *22*, pp. 54–58, and statement by Busemann in Foreword to Yaglom and Boltyanskiĭ *74*, p. v. Also see sections devoted to *intuition* in Allendoerfer *2*.

10. Additional problems where line coordinates are useful will be found in Winger *70*, pp. 25, 26.

11. For a discussion of the technical meaning of the term *model* as used in present-day mathematics, see Eves *22*, pp. 396–97.

12. If the reader enjoyed *Alice in Wonderland* and *Through the Looking-glass*, and has not seen *The Annotated Alice* with Introduction and Notes by Martin Gardner (New York: Clarkson N. Potter, Inc., 1960), he has a treat in store for himself.

13. In the terms of modern algebra, we are dealing with an equivalence relation and equivalence classes here. See Rosenbaum *56*, pp. 42–44.

14. For an exposition of vectors, together with an exploitation of these in geometry, see Robinson *55*, or Schuster *60*.

15. Such a rectangular array is called a *matrix*, and the literature on these is very extensive. Introductory presentations are given by L. E. Fuller, *Basic Matrix Theory* (Englewood Cliffs, N.J.: Prentice-Hall, Inc. 1962), and by W. V. Parker and J. C. Eaves, *Matrices* (New York: The Ronald Press Company, 1960).

16. For additional models of the projective plane and for a discussion of the projective plane as a closed, one-sided, non-orientable surface, see Hilbert and Cohn-Vossen *36* p. 306ff. Also see Barr *8*.

17. Likewise a carelessly drawn figure can lead to a false conclusion. See Adler *1* pp. 23, 24 for a proof of the theorem *Every triangle is isosceles*.

18. See Argunov and Skornyakov *3* pp. 1–3 for a description of *configuration theorem*.

19. When he was writing this section, it occurred to the author that an interesting set of puzzles or solitaire games could be devised that would be not only entertaining but also instructive. The Library of Science, 59 Fourth Avenue, New York, N.Y., will publish and distribute these puzzles under the title *Configurations—Number Puzzles and Pastimes for All Ages*. Although the puzzles do not require any previous knowledge of mathematical topics, readers of this book will find that they amplify and extend many of the ideas expressed in Section II.3.

20. Actually this is very much the way in which Pascal discovered the theorem. See Smith *64*, pp. 326–30.

21. Recent books on the foundations of geometry include G. de B. Robinson, *The Foundations of Geometry* (4th ed.) (Toronto: University of Toronto Press, 1959), Karol Borsuk and Wanda Szmielew, *Foundations of Geometry*, (Amsterdam: North-Holland Publishing Company, 1960), and Howard Levi, *Foundations of Geometry and Trigonometry* (Englewood Cliffs, N.J.: Prentice-Hall, Inc., 1960).

22. For additional problems involving inaccessible points and lines see Argunov and Skornyakov *3*, pp. 29–36.

23. Using the notation of Fig. 46, let us call the Pappus line l_3, keep the original order for the points A_1, B_1, C_1 on l_1, but consider each of the five additional orders by which we can label the three points on l_2. To each of these new orders will correspond a new Pappus line so that altogether we shall have six such lines l_3, l_4, ..., l_8. Steiner proved in 1832 that the three Pascal lines corresponding to the orders A_2, B_2, C_2; B_2, C_2, A_2; C_2, A_2, B_2 on l_2 meet in a point, say D, and that the remaining three meet in another point, say E. If now we omit from the figure the lines l_1, l_2 and the points $A_1, B_1, C_1, A_2, B_2, C_2$ but add the points D and E, we have a $20_3 \, 15_4$ configuration. For a picture of this *complete figure for the theorem of Pappus*, see Baker *6*, II, 216.

24. In a two-part article entitled "Desargues and his strange theorem,"

(*Scripta Mathematica*, XX (1954) No. 1–2, 3–4, pp. 1–18), N. A. Court states:

> But the most striking thing about this amazing theorem is its fertility. By that I do not have reference to the consequences of the theorem, rich and far reaching as they are. What I do want to point out is how much can be said about the simple figure formed by the two perspective triangles. The following two sections may serve as illustrations.

Court then discusses in considerable detail the fascinating topics, *Multiply Perspective Triangles* (see also Winger 70, pp. 102–4 and Veblen and Young 67, pp. 247–49), and *Veronesian Systems of Triangles.*

Instead of describing these, we mention some additional properties or theorems connected with the configuration of Desargues. The reader may enjoy drawing figures for some of these.

The configuration of Desargues can be regarded (in five ways) as consisting of a complete 4-point and a complete 4-line so situated that the six sides of the 4-line pass through the six vertices of the 4-point. Using the notation of Fig. 62, one of these complete 4-points is 12, 13, 14, 15 and the corresponding 4-line is 234, 235, 245, 345.

The configuration of Desargues can be regarded (in six ways) as consisting of two pentagons so situated that the consecutive sides of each pass through alternate vertices of the other. One of these pairs of pentagons is 12, 23, 34, 45, 51; 31, 14, 42, 25, 53.

The configuration of Desargues can be regarded as a self-inscribed and self-circumscribed decagon where the sides belong alternately to two mutually inscribed pentagons (see Hilbert and Cohn-Vossen *36*, p. 127). One of these decagons is 13, 15, 14, 34, 24, 12, 25, 45, 35, 23.

If three triangles are perspective from the same point, the three axes of perspectivity of the three pairs of triangles are concurrent, and conversely. The figure for this is the $20_3 \, 15_4$ configuration that we encountered when studying the complete figure for the theorem of Pappus (see Note 23).

The above theorem can be dualized to give a $15_4\,20_3$ configuration. It has also been extended as follows (Veronese, *Atti dei Lincei* 1876–77, p. 649). Nine points, located in sets of three each on three concurrent lines, form 36 sets of three perspective triangles. For each set of three distinct triangles the axes of perspectivity meet in a point; and the 36 points thus obtained lie in sets of four on 27 lines, thus giving a $36_4\,27_3$ configuration.

And finally, there are such tree-planting problems as the following (Winger *70*, p. 104). Show how to plant (a) 25 trees in 10 rows with 6 trees in a row (answer: use the configuration of Desargues with the additional intersections of the lines); (b) 19 trees in 9 rows with 5 trees in a row (answer: omit one line of the configuration of Desargues and its intersections, but as in the preceding case, use the additional intersections of the other lines). Corresponding problems can, of course, be made up using the configuration of Pappus.

25. For two different methods of finding the equations of a conic through five points, see L. J. Adams, and P. A. White, *Analytic Geometry and Calculus* (New York: Oxford University Press, 1961), pp. 279, 280.

26. The problem of determining the number of different hexagons obtainable from six points is equivalent to the problem of finding the number of different arrangements fox six keys on a key ring— a problem that is discussed in the chapter on permutations in secondary school algebra texts.

27. Concerning the figure for the 60 Pascal lines, Baker (*7*, p. 349) states:

> *It has finally been found that the best and simplest view of the figure of sixty lines is obtainable from a figure of fifteen lines in a space of four dimensions, which are such as to meet in threes in fifteen points, of which each line contains three of these points. For an exposition of this higher figure, we refer the reader to* Principles of Geometry, *Vol. II, pp. 219–36.*

This reference is to Baker *6*, and the 15₃ configuration of the quotation is used as the frontispiece for volume II and is entitled HEXA-GRAMMUM MYSTICUM.

28. The reader who is familiar with *modular fields* and *Galois fields* will recognize that there are applications here. For the beginner, the following articles by B. W. Jones are recommended, "Miniature number systems," *Math. Teacher*, v. 51 (1958), pp. 226–31, and "Miniature geometries," *Math. Teacher*, v. 52 (1959), pp. 66–71.

29. The reader may now be interested in examining the 8₃ configuration from the analytic point of view. Using the notation of Fig. 38 (page 76), the following choice of points is suggested

$$1\ (1, 0, 0) \qquad\qquad 5\ (0, 0, 1)$$
$$2\ (1, 1, a + 1) \qquad 6\ (1, 1, 0)$$
$$3\ (1, a + 1, a) \qquad 7\ (0, 1, 0)$$
$$4\ (1, 0, a) \qquad\qquad 8\ (0, 1, 1).$$

The lines of the configuration will then turn out to be

$$[1]\ (a + 1)x_2 - x_3 = 0 \qquad [5]\ x_1 - x_2 = 0$$
$$[2]\ x_2 = 0 \qquad\qquad\qquad [6]\ ax_1 - x_3 = 0$$
$$[3]\ x_3 = 0 \qquad\qquad\qquad [7]\ x_1 - x_2 + x_3 = 0$$
$$[4]\ ax_1 + x_2 - x_3 = 0 \qquad [8]\ x_1 = 0$$

provided a is taken as one of the complex cube roots of unity, i.e. provided $a = -\frac{1}{2} + (\sqrt{3}/2)i$, or $a = -\frac{1}{2} - (\sqrt{3}/2)i$.

30. For some interesting finite geometries, other than those given by the finite planes with $n + 1$ points on a line, see Eves *22*, pp. 426–33.

31. Gardner *26* (pp. 183–84) gives a brief description of how Latin squares can be used in agricultural research. Additional references on the design and analysis of experiments are to R. A. Fisher, *The Design of Experiments* (London: Oliver and Boyd, 1935), and H. B. Mann, *Analysis and Design of Experiments* (New York: Dover Publications, Inc., 1949).

Bibliography

1. Adler, C. F., *Modern Geometry, an Integrated First Course*. New York: McGraw-Hill Book Company, 1958.

2. Allendoerfer, C. B., "The Narrow Mathematician," *The American Mathematical Monthly*, LXIX (June–July, 1962), 461–69.

3. Argunov, B. I. and L. A. Skornyakov, *Configuration Theorems*, tr. by E. E. Enochs and R. B. Brown. Boston: D. C. Heath & Company, 1963.

4. Arnold, B. H., *Intuitive Concepts in Elementary Topology*. Englewood Cliffs, N.J.: Prentice-Hall, Inc., 1962.

5. Baer, R., *Linear Algebra and Projective Geometry*. New York: Academic Press, Inc., 1952.

6. Baker, H. F., *Principles of Geometry*. 6 vols. New York: Cambridge University Press, 1922–33.

7. ———, *An Introduction to Plane Geometry*. New York: Cambridge University Press, 1943.

8. Barr, Stephen, *Experiments in Topology*. New York: Thomas Y. Crowell Company, 1964.

9. Bell, E. T., *The Development of Mathematics* (2nd ed.). New York: McGraw-Hill Book Company, 1945.

10. Bing, R. H., *Elementary Point Set Topology*, Herbert Ellsworth Slaught Memorial Paper No. 8. Buffalo, N.Y.: The Mathematical Association of America, Inc., 1960.

11. Blumenthal, L. M., *Theory and Applications of Distance Geometry*. Oxford: Clarendon Press, 1953.

12. ———, *A Modern View of Geometry*. San Francisco: W. H. Freeman and Company, 1961.

13. Bruck, R. H. and H. J. Ryser, "The Nonexistence of Certain Finite Projective Planes," *Canadian Journal of Mathematics*, I (March, 1949), 88–93.

14. Busemann, H., "The Role of Geometry for the Mathematics Student," *American Mathematical Monthly*, LXVII (March, 1960), 281–85.

15. Coolidge, J. L., "Heroic Age of Geometry," *Bulletin of the American Mathematical Society*, XXXV (January-February, 1929), 19–37.

16. Courant, R. and H. Robbins, *What is Mathematics?* New York: Oxford University Press, 1941.

17. Coxeter, H. S. M., "Self-dual Configurations and Regular Graphs," *Bulletin of the American Mathematical Society*, LVI (September, 1950), 413–55.

18. ———, *The Real Projective Plane* (2nd ed.). New York: Cambridge University Press, 1955. Students' Edition (paperback), 1960.

19. ———, *Introduction to Geometry*. New York: John Wiley & Sons, Inc., 1961.

20. ——, *Projective Geometry*. New York: Blaisdell Publishing Company, 1964.

21. Delachet, A., *Contemporary Geometry*, tr. by H. G. Bergmann. New York: Dover Publications, Inc., 1962.

22. Eves, H., *A Survey of Geometry*, Vol. I. Boston: Allyn and Bacon, Inc., 1963. Vol. II, 1965.

23. —— and C. V. Newsom, *An Introduction to the Foundations and Fundamental Concepts of Mathematics*. New York: Holt, Rinehart, and Winston, Inc., 1958.

24. Félix, L., *The Modern Aspect of Mathematics*, tr. by J. H. and F. H. Hlavaty. New York: Basic Books, Inc., 1960.

25. Fishback, W. T., *Projective and Euclidean Geometry*. New York: John Wiley & Sons, Inc., 1962.

26. Gardner, M., "How Three Modern Mathematicians Disproved a Celebrated Conjecture of Leonhard Euler," *Scientific American*, CCI (November, 1959), 181–88.

27. Gerretsen, J. C. H., *Lectures on Tensor Calculus and Differential Geometry*. Groningen, Netherlands: Noordhoff, 1962.

28. Graustein, W. C., *Introduction to Higher Geometry*. New York: The Macmillan Company, 1930.

29. Hall, Marshall, Jr., "Projective Planes," *Trans. Amer. Math. Soc.* LIV (September, 1943), 229–77. "Correction," *Trans. Amer. Math. Soc.*, LXV (May, 1949), 473–74.

30. ——, *Projective Planes and Related Topics*. Pasadena: California Institute of Technology, 1954.

31. ——, "Finite Projective Planes," in *Contributions to Geometry*, Herbert Ellsworth Slaught Memorial Paper No. 4, pp. 18–24. Buffalo, N.Y.: The Mathematical Association of America, Inc., 1955.

32. ———, *The Theory of Groups*. New York: The Macmillan Company, 1959.

33. ———, *Combinatorial Analysis*. New York: Blaisdell Publishing Company, (To be published).

34. Heyting, A., *Axiomatic Projective Geometry*. Amsterdam: North-Holland Publishing Company (New York: Interscience Publishers), 1963.

35. Hilbert, D., *The Foundations of Geometry*, tr. by E. J. Townsend. Chicago: The Open Court Publishing Company, 1902.

36. ——— and S. Cohn-Vossen, *Geometry and the Imagination*, tr. by P. Nemenyi. New York: Chelsea Publishing Company, 1952.

37. Ivins, W. M. Jr., *Art and Geometry—A Study in Space Intuitions*. Cambridge, Mass.: Harvard University Press, 1946. Reprinted by Dover Publications, Inc., 1964.

38. James, G., ed., *The Tree of Mathematics*. Pacioma, Calif.: The Digest Press, 1957.

39. Jenner, W. E., *Rudiments of Algebraic Geometry*. New York: Oxford University Press, 1963.

40. Kasner, E. and J. Newman, *Mathematics and the Imagination*. New York: Simon and Schuster, Inc., 1940.

41. Klein, F., *Elementary Mathematics from an Advanced Standpoint*, Vol. II, *Geometry*, tr. by E. R. Hedrick and C. A. Noble. New York: Dover Publications, Inc., 1939. First German edition published in 1908.

42. Kline, M., *Mathematics in Western Culture*. New York: Oxford University Press, 1953.

43. Kuiper, N. H., *Linear Algebra and Geometry*. Amsterdam: North-Holland Publishing Company (New York: Interscience Publishers Inc.), 1962.

44. Lehmer, D. N., *An Elementary Course in Synthetic Projective Geometry*. Boston: Ginn and Company, 1917.

45. Levi, F., *Geometrische Konfigurationen*. Leipzig: S. Hirzel, 1929.

46. Levy, Harry, *Projective and Related Geometries*. New York: The Macmillan Company, 1964.

47. Mansfield, M. J., *Introduction to Topology*. Princeton, N.J.: D. Van Nostrand Co. Inc., 1963.

48. Meserve, B. E., *Fundamental Concepts of Geometry*. Reading, Mass.: Addison-Wesley Publishing Company, Inc., 1955.

49. Moise, E. E., *Elementary Geometry from an Advanced Standpoint*. Reading, Mass.: Addison-Wesley Publishing Company, Inc., 1963.

50. Niven, I., *Mathematics: a House Built on Sand?* Eugene, Oregon: University of Oregon Books, 1959.

51. Patterson, B. C., *Projective Geometry*. New York: John Wiley & Sons, Inc., 1937.

52. Pedoe, Daniel, *An Introduction to Projective Geometry*. New York: The Macmillan Company, 1963.

53. Perfect, Hazel, *Topics in Geometry*. New York: The Macmillan Company, 1963.

54. Pickert, Günter, *Projektive Ebenen*. Berlin: Springer-Verlag, 1955.

55. Robinson, G. deB., *Vector Geometry*. Boston: Allyn and Bacon, Inc., 1962.

56. Rosenbaum, R. A., *Introduction to Projective Geometry and Modern Algebra*. Reading, Mass.: Addison-Wesley Publishing Company, Inc., 1963.

57. Ryser, H. J., "Geometries and Incidence Matrices," in *Contributions to Geometry*, Herbert Ellsworth Slaught Memorial Paper No. 4,

pp. 25–31. Buffalo, N.Y.: The Mathematical Association of America, Inc., 1955.

58. ———, *Combinatorial Mathematics*. The Carus Mathematical Monographs, No. 14. Published by The Mathematical Association of America, Inc. New York: John Wiley & Sons, Inc., 1963.

59. Schreier, O. and E. Sperner, *Projective Geometry of n Dimensions*, Vol. II of *Introduction to Modern Algebra and Matrix Theory*. New York: Chelsea Publishing Company, 1961.

60. Schuster, S., *Elementary Vector Geometry*. New York: John Wiley & Sons, Inc., 1962.

61. Seidenberg, A., *Lectures in Projective Geometry*. Princeton, N.J.: D. Van Nostrand Co. Inc., 1962.

62. Skornyakov, L. A., "Projective planes," in *Translations*, Series one, Volume I, *Algebra*. Providence: American Mathematical Society, 1962.

63. Singer, J., "A Theorem in Finite Projective Geometry and Some Applications to Number Theory," *Trans. of the Am. Math. Soc.*, XLIII (May, 1938), 377–85.

64. Smith, D. E., *A Source Book in Mathematics*. New York: McGraw-Hill Book Company, 1929.

65. Springer, C. E., *Geometry and Analysis of Projective Spaces*. San Francisco: W. H. Freeman and Company, 1964.

66. Stone, M. H., "The Revolution in Mathematics," *Liberal Education*, XLVII (May, 1961), 304–27.

67. Veblen, O. and J. W. Young, *Projective Geometry*. 2 vols. Boston: Ginn & Company, 1910, 1918.

68. Von Neumann, J., *Continuous Geometry*. Princeton, N.J.: Princeton University Press, 1960.

69. Wesson, J. R., "Finite Plane Projective Geometries," in *Contributions to Geometry*, Herbert Ellsworth Slaught Memorial Paper No. 4, pp. 32–40. Buffalo, N.Y.: The Mathematical Association of America, Inc., 1955.

70. Winger, R. M., *An Introduction to Projective Geometry*. Boston: D. C. Heath & Company, 1923. Reprinted by Dover Publications, Inc., 1962.

71. Wolfe, H. E., *Introduction to Non-Euclidean Geometry*. New York: The Dryden Press, Inc., 1945.

72. Woods, F. S., *Higher Geometry*. Boston: Ginn and Company, 1922. Reprinted by Dover Publications, Inc., 1961.

73. Yaglom, I. M., *Geometric Transformations*, New Mathematical Library, No. 8, tr. by Allen Shields. New York: Random House, 1962.

74. ——— and V. G. Boltyanskiĭ, *Convex Figures*, Library of the Mathematical Circle, Vol. IV, tr. by P. J. Kelly and L. F. Walton. New York: Holt, Rinehart, and Winston, Inc., 1961.

Index